Kids
SPEAK
11

chaim walder

Translated by
Aviva Rappaport

Illustrated by
Devorah Benedict

Originally published in 2019 in Hebrew as
Yeladim Mesaprim al Atzmam (Vol. 11)

First published 2019
ISBN 978-1-68025-395-5

Translated by Aviva Rappaport
Illustrated by Devorah Benedict

Feldheim Publishers
POB 43163 / Jerusalem, Israel

208 Airport Executive Park
Nanuet, NY 10954

www.feldheim.com

Distributed in Europe by:
Lehmanns
+44-0-191-430-0333
info@lehmanns.co.uk
www.lehmanns.co.uk

Distributed in Australia by:
Golds World of Judaica
+613 95278775
info@golds.com.au
www.golds.com.au

Printed in Israel

To my family in the United States:
Yaakov and Tova Mendelowitz and family,
Avraham Yosef and Pessi Frankel and family,
my cousin Leizer Mendelowitz and his wife,
and my nephew Ari Berkowitz, publisher,
The Voice of Lakewood, and his wife.

Contents

True Brothers

My name is Muli. (That's short for Shmuli).

I'm thirteen, and I live in Connecticut.

This story is about my brother Ruli (short for Yisrael) and me. We're twins.

But don't think this is going to be a story about twins who look so alike that everyone mixes them up. It's not, because we're not identical.

No one has ever guessed that we're twins. Even once we tell them, they're still surprised.

Why? Because one of us is tall and the other is short. One of us has dark hair, and the other's is light. One of us is chubby, and the other is skinny. You get the picture. We're the least identical twins you've ever seen.

There are other differences, too—differences that I think are far more significant than looks.

Ruli is a top student, popular, great at sports, and a leader.

And I'm...the opposite. Learning is hard for me. I try, but it's been a struggle from the start. Ruli knew how to read in kindergarten, while I only caught on in second grade. His grades are always the best in the class; mine are always the worst.

I'm not good at sports, either. I can't run fast, catch a ball, or do anything really well. Socially, chances are that if not for Ruli, no one would pay any attention to me. I'd be sitting on the sidelines, alone and lonely. But fortunately, Ruli doesn't let that happen. He makes sure I'm included in everything, and he never spends time with friends without including me. If it takes me longer to get ready in the morning because I'm a little slower, he'd rather miss the bus than go without me.

I always tell him, "Ruli, you go on ahead. Why should you be late because of me?"

But he says, "Muli, don't worry. I don't like going alone. Hurry up, and we'll take the next bus."

When I think of how much Ruli gives me, my heart swells with love and appreciation. But when I think of how much he loses out on because of me, I'm so embarrassed. Usually, I keep all these emotions inside because when I thank him, he asks me to please stop it.

He says he's the one who gains by spending time with me because I'm the "best" and "loyal" and all kinds of stuff that he makes up just to make me feel good. Telling him how much he's losing out is just about the only thing guaranteed to make him annoyed at me. So I keep everything to myself, but inside, I really appreciate him.

* * *

The story I want to tell you happened last summer in camp. Every year, my brother and I and our friends go to a sleepaway camp in the Catskills organized by our school for a month or two.

Our school places us in different groups according to our level of learning. Months before vacation starts, we take a test, and we're placed in groups based on our scores. Every group has a different track in learning, sports, and activities.

There are a couple of reasons why they do it this way. One reason is that two months is a long time, and the directors say it gives us a better camp experience if we spend our time with boys on our level. But everyone knows there's another reason, one that's probably the main reason: we all work extra hard throughout the year, hoping to get into the highest-level group. It's an honor to be chosen for that group, but even better, most of the major activities and sports events happen there. If you're chosen to be in the top level, you're a winner. And if you're placed in the lowest level, it's almost a punishment.

I spent the whole year dreading the test. I knew I wouldn't do well on it, and then I'd be placed in the lowest level. I thought about it a lot—and it didn't give me the greatest feeling.

I didn't discuss it with Ruli, and I noticed that whenever anyone mentioned camp, he changed the subject. That made me realize that he was afraid of the same thing I was afraid of: that they'd separate us.

* * *

The day of the test arrived, and a few hundred boys came to take it. We sat at long tables in a large auditorium, and proctors walked around the whole time to make sure no one cheated.

Ruli sat down next to me. He wrote and wrote. I wrote what I knew, which wasn't much.

I saw that Ruli had finished his test and was waiting for me to finish mine. It took me a while, but finally, I was done.

Ruli asked me to bring him a glass of water, and I

went to get it. Then we handed our tests to the person in charge.

We went home in silence. That silence was filled with a lot of unspoken words, things we could have said but didn't.

The next few days were tense. We didn't say a word about the test we'd taken, the results, or what would happen after they told us the results.

A week later we were called into the school office. Waiting there was a man we'd never seen before, a representative of the camp we'd signed up for. He told us to sit down.

"I asked to speak to both of you before you get the results," he said, "so that we can see what to do.

"I understand that you're twins and very close to each other. But there's a problem. One of you scored high and the other…a lot lower. According to our rules, we have to separate you."

I can't say he told us anything new.

"You're Muli, right?" he said to me. "Muli is short for Shmuel, correct?"

"Yes," I said heavily, waiting for the harsh decree.

"Well, you got one of the highest marks of all the boys who applied. There's no doubt that you will be placed in the highest group."

I was shocked. It couldn't be. It had to be a mistake!

"And you, Ruli," he said to my twin brother, "that's short for Yisrael, correct?"

Brilliant. How did he ever guess?

"I'm sorry to have to tell you this, but your mark wasn't good enough. You'll have to be in the second group."

I felt the room spin around me. Impossible. It just didn't make sense.

He handed us our tests. One look at mine told me everything.

The test he handed me was Ruli's test. But the name at the top was mine: Muli. Interestingly, there were no signs of erasing or any other changes.

"Sir," I said, "there's been a mistake."

"I'm sorry," he said as he gathered the papers into a neat pile, "but there's been no mistake. There are whole questions that were left unanswered. Even this low mark was generous, believe me."

"But—" I began.

"I'm sorry," he interrupted, "but I have neither the time nor the energy for discussions. If you wish, you may appeal the results in writing, though I don't know why you'd want to appeal this. It's your brother who has the problem."

A second before we left, I said to him, "Can I ask you a small question?"

"Sure," he said.

"Did you know us before we walked into the room?"

He looked surprised by the question. "No, I didn't know you. I'm not from Connecticut."

"Then how did you know that I'm Muli? As soon as we walked in you said to me, 'You're Muli.' How did you know?"

Now he looked even more surprised. His face flushed. It seemed like he had an answer but didn't want to say it.

"Please," I said. "Just answer the question."

"Um, let's just say I drew a conclusion."

"It was because I'm taller, right?" I said. "Because Ruli is short and chubby, you thought to yourself, 'The tall one must be the successful one.' True?"

The man (who wasn't in *chinuch,* but was helping the camp with this administrative work) turned red. "The truth is…uh…that is correct."

To Ruli, he said, "I apologize. I had no idea…"

It was embarrassing.

Then I decided to say to him, "What if I tell you that the test I'm holding in my hand wasn't written by

me? It was written by Ruli, who, of the two of us, is the outstanding one. He's the one who's better at sports, king of the class and everything. The test that Ruli is holding is my test. As tall and impressive looking as I may be, would you believe that I don't come to his ankles?"

He was in shock. A heavy silence filled the room.

"You shouldn't have told him," Ruli said.

"Why—" One look at Ruli and I had my answer. "You took the test in my name to begin with. When you sent me out to bring a glass of water, you switched tests with me and changed the letter M to R so that I'd get a high mark."

Ruli turned bright red and didn't answer.

The camp representative looked at Ruli and then at me in astonishment.

"Why would you do something like that?" he asked Ruli. "I've seen instances where someone tried to cheat, but why would an outstanding student like you pretend to fail a test?"

Ruli didn't answer.

I looked at the man. Tears filled his eyes.

"You don't have to answer," he said. "The question is the answer. You did it for your brother. You couldn't stand to see him placed in the lower level, so you chose to go there yourself, instead of him." By now he was crying. He sat there and cried.

I'd never seen a grown man cry like that.

Ruli and I didn't know what to do with ourselves.

He took a tissue and dried his eyes. "I have children," he said. "But they're not friends like you two are. They're jealous and fight and can't stand each other. I never would have believed I'd meet brothers who love each other and care about each other as much as you two do." His sobbed and then said, "How did your parents merit having such children? How?"

We didn't know what to say. For us, it was the most natural thing in the world. We never thought you could feel differently toward a brother.

He calmed down and said, "Listen to me. The test doesn't interest me in the least. It's nothing compared to the real test you withstood: the test of life. Both of you will be placed in the highest level. Not as a favor, but because you deserve it. Your good *middos* are far beyond the highest level. But I have one condition."

We stood straighter to hear his condition.

"I'm putting my two boys in your bunk. I want them to see you and stick close to you so that they can see how wonderful it is when brothers act like real brothers. Let them learn to love each other from the way you act and from who you are. Having children who love each other is the greatest gift any parent could hope for."

* * *

That's the story.

Ruli and I were together in the same group that summer. We had a blast. We had to bunk with a pair of enemies who happened to be brothers, but by the end of the first month, they were no longer enemies. At least we repaid our debt to their father.

Aside from our parents, no one knew how both of us made it into the highest level. But after the change we saw in our roommates, we thought our story should appear in *Kids Speak*. We want as many kids as possible to know about it. It's possible to be loyal, devoted, caring, and loving to your brother. Not only is it possible, but it's also the best way to be. Ruli and I are brothers, heart and soul. I'd do anything for him—and he'd do the same for me.

Between Heaven and Earth

My name is Tali.

I'm twelve, and I live in Beit Shemesh.

The story I'm going to tell you, about what happened to me and my friend, is a real cliffhanger. (Not exactly, but close enough.) Soon you'll see what I mean.

But first, I want to tell you something that might not seem connected to the story but that you'll soon see is.

At the time my story took place, the atmosphere in our class wasn't great. There was a lot of *lashon hara* and *rechilus* going on, plus a lot of silent power struggles between girls.

The teachers tried to stop it. They taught us the laws of *lashon hara* and *rechilus* and talked to us about the damage speaking improperly can cause. It helped, but not for long. It was just too hard to resist the temptation.

Now for the story.

* * *

It was *chol hamoed* Pesach. My friend Noa called to invite my little sister Shulamis and me to her house. I asked my mother for permission to go, and she said, "No problem, as long as someone is home." (My parents have a rule that they only let us go to friends' houses if at least one parent is home.)

Without thinking, I said, "Sure."

I had no idea whether Noa's parents were home or not; I only answered my mother that way so she'd let me go. I didn't feel like I was lying. Maybe Noa's parents *were* home. They could have been…

I know that sounds stupid, but I wanted to go to Noa's house, so I said it.

I took my sister Shulamis, and three minutes later we were at Noa's. She lives in the building next to ours on the fifth floor.

Even now, as I'm telling you the story, I'm starting to shake. Because what I'm about to tell you is not that simple. At all.

When the story took place, Noa's house was undergoing renovations. Her parents had decided to enclose the porch off the living room and turn it into another bedroom. They'd put up walls, and there were two windows, both with metal window guards on the outside. At the time, these window guards weren't installed. They were just set in place, waiting for the final installation. But we didn't know that.

Another thing before takeoff (my choice of words is deliberate): The door between the living room and the porch wasn't the actual door but a temporary one for use during the renovations, and it could only be opened from the living room, not from the porch.

Noa and I made a fake Kiddush for our three-year-old sisters in the living room, complete with fancy napkins, a plastic goblet, water instead of wine, and cake instead of challah. When we finished, we went out to the porch.

I was the last one out, and without thinking, I automatically pulled the door closed behind me. I didn't realize that meant we wouldn't be able to open it.

Noa didn't notice that I'd closed the door.

As if we hadn't made enough mistakes for one day, now we made the biggest mistake ever: We started to climb up onto the windowsill to sit in the window guard.

Take my word for it: Don't ever do this! Not in a million years, no matter how old you are, and certainly not if you're ten and weigh what a ten-year-old weighs.

Noa stood on a chair and jumped into the window guard "shelf" at the bottom, and then I heard her say, "Tali!"

"I'm coming," I said, and before Noa could stop me, I'd already jumped in too.

As soon as I landed, Noa didn't have to tell me a thing.

The window guard moved. It was loose. We didn't have to know a lot about window guards to know that this one wasn't connected to the wall normally.

We both stared at the growing space between the window guard and the wall, and we realized that just two small screws stood between us and…

The ground five floors below.

* * *

What would you do if it happened to you? You'd scream, right?

Good thing you weren't there. Because if you had been, you would have realized that it was impossible to scream. The window guard was hanging by a thread. Any movement on our part could send it—and us—falling five stories below.

We didn't dare make a peep.

But the terror showed in our eyes. We both knew

our lives were in danger and that any movement could cause a tragedy.

I slowly put a finger to my lips, signaling Noa "shhh." Then, using my calmest voice, I said to my sister, "Shulamis, can you please go into the house and bring me the phone?"

Shulamis didn't yet know that our lives were in danger. She turned to go into the living room.

"The door won't open," I heard her say.

"Push hard," I said in my quietest voice, not moving a muscle. I didn't know that the door didn't open from our side.

Noa shook her head ever so slightly.

I didn't know what she was trying to say.

Shulamis pushed harder on the door, but nothing happened.

"The door can only be opened from inside," Noa whispered.

The window guard moved.

"Help!" we screamed—and then realized that our shouts had just made it worse.

That's when Shulamis and Miri realized that something was going on.

"Why don't you come down, Tali?" Shulamis asked me.

I didn't reply. I could hardly breathe.

"Noa, come down." Shulamis started to cry. "We want to go back to the living room and finish the Kiddush."

She and Noa's sister, Miri, both started crying and screaming. "Get down! We want to go inside!"

I don't think anyone can understand how terrified we were.

There we were, hanging five stories above the ground, trapped on the balcony with two little kids who were hysterical, and we couldn't even shout because if we did, the window guard would shake loose and fall.

We looked at each other wordlessly. I saw tears on Noa's cheeks and realized that I was crying, too.

I looked down. I saw my apartment on the ground floor in the other building. Then I looked straight ahead and saw the hills of Yerushalayim in the distance, and that reminded me of a *tehillah* that fit our situation perfectly.

I started to say it softly: *Shir hama'alos, esa einai el heharim, me'ayin yavo ezri…*

When I finished, I took a deep breath and said in a whisper, "Shulamis, listen to me and do exactly what I tell you."

Shulamis recognized the words and the tone of voice. When I talked to her like that, she knew I meant business.

She stopped crying.

"I want you and Miri to play the game of 'One, two, three—Miri!'"

She knew the game. When we wanted to call Miri down to play, we'd shout, "One, two, three—Miiirrriii!"

She and Miri called out together, "One, two, three—Miiirrriii!"

"Good," I said, still talking barely above a whisper. "Now shout, 'One, two, three—HELP!'"

Miri and Shulamis started to scream, "One, two, three—HELP!"

"Again," I said.

They screamed again.

"Now scream it as loud as you can," I said, and even tried smiling. (I'm glad you can't see that smile because it was the scariest smile ever. Not that the three-year-olds realized it.)

"One, two, three—HELP!"

A window opened in our building.

A neighbor looked out. It took her a few seconds to realize what was going on.

I pointed to the loose screws.

"Oh no!" I heard her cry. She froze in shock for

a second, but then she started shouting, "Help! Call Hatzalah!"

Within seconds, more neighbors appeared at the windows. We signaled that we were in trouble, and they called Hatzalah, the fire department, the police, and an ambulance.

Meanwhile, someone ran to tell my mother what was going on. Within minutes, my father took the elevator to the roof and from there jumped down onto the balcony.

As he moved closer to us, I said, "Abba, be careful. Even the slightest movement can make the window guard fall."

"I see that," my father said calmly. "I'm going to hold the window guard and pull it to the wall. Don't worry. *B'ezras Hashem,* I'll be strong enough to hold both the window guard and you two. My hands will hold it instead of the two screws, and you can jump down."

My father walked up to the window guard. I looked at him. I saw that he was concentrating and tense, but the look in his eyes gave me confidence. He knew what he was doing.

He grabbed the window guard with both hands, and immediately we felt more secure. My father's

strong hands pulled the window guard to the wall.

Abba signaled Noa to get down first. That's my father, and that's how he raises us kids: Help the other person first and then worry about yourself.

"Don't be afraid," he said. "Stand up and jump down to the floor."

Noa hesitated.

"It's okay," I told her. "You can trust my father."

"B'ezras Hashem," my father said.

Noa stood on the window guard shelf. I saw the muscles of my father's hands tense with the effort, but you couldn't see a thing on his face.

Noa jumped down. She was safe!

"Now," my father said to me, "just grab hold of me, and I'll take you down."

I clung to him like I'd never clung to anything in my life. He moved back and let me slide down to the balcony floor. Then he tried to bring the window guard inside, but it couldn't get through the opening. The empty window guard fell five stories down, crashed onto the ground, and broke into pieces.

And to think we had just been standing on it…

Noa and I started to cry, then Shulamis and Miri too. As young as they were, they understood that a miracle had just taken place.

My father was very moved. He murmured words of gratitude to Hashem for saving us.

At home, we talked about everything. My parents reassured me and didn't say anything, but there was something I felt I had to get off my chest.

"Abba, I know I didn't act right. I didn't tell Ima the truth. I let her think that Noa's parents were home without checking to make sure. What I went through taught me how important it is to listen to your parents. If I had listened to you, I wouldn't have gotten into such a dangerous situation, and someone inside the house would have quickly rescued us."

My parents didn't say a word. They saw that I'd gotten the message.

* * *

Everyone was talking about it. Everyone wanted to hear us describe those moments of sheer terror.

At first, it was hard for me and Noa to talk about it. But as we retold the story again and again, it lost its terrifying grip over us.

A week later, we made a *seudas hodayah* in class.

The teacher spoke about *hashgachah pratis* and about how Hashem constantly takes care of every one of His children. She also quoted a different *tehillah*, and said, *"Shomer pesa'im Hashem*—Hashem takes care of His children who sometimes do things because they don't know any better." It was a subtle rebuke because a *"pesi"* is a fool.

But I wasn't offended. I knew I deserved it.

Then the teacher surprised us by asking Noa and me if we wanted to add anything.

We didn't think we'd be asked to speak, so we hadn't prepared for it. Noa said she preferred that I speak for both of us.

Maybe you'll be surprised, but I actually had something to say.

"I've been thinking all week about those minutes of utter terror on the window guard," I began, "and I think there's something we can all learn from it."

The classroom got very quiet.

"Over the past few months, our teachers have been talking to us a lot about refraining from forbidden speech like *lashon hara* and *rechilus*. Like everyone else, I knew I was supposed to guard my speech, but I can't say I never slipped up. And I think it's because I never actually understood what speech could do. But there, on the window guard, I realized that every single word Noa and I said did mean something.

"The air we breathe in and out when we talk causes

our bodies to move. We didn't dare shout because that would have shaken the window guard. We thought very carefully before we let even a single word out of our mouths. There was one time when Noa and I looked at each other, and our tears spoke for us.

"I've been thinking about it all week. I feel like Hashem sent me a message about the power of speech. I think if each of us was as careful with her words as if she was saying them while standing on a shaky window guard, none of us would say any *lashon hara*. Because when you think about speech and what it can cause, not a single girl who has *yiras shamayim* would say it."

A few heads nodded.

"All forbidden speech is said when we're not paying attention to what we're saying, and the results are sometimes just as destructive as a window guard that's hanging by a thread. Maybe a person's life isn't at stake with every word we say, but his soul definitely is. I'm grateful to Hashem for the miracle that saved me, and I know that Noa is too. And I hope that what I just said will make everyone in our class weigh their words, and that will be a *zechus* for us."

When I finished, no one said a word. Many girls had tears in their eyes. I sensed that the message had gotten through.

The teacher started clapping, and the whole class joined in.

* * *

Now, two years later, I'd like to pass on this message to girls everywhere in the world: The ability to talk is amazing. You don't need to be silent. You can and should talk to express yourself and share with others. But when it comes to harmful speech, weigh each word. Imagine that you or the person you're talking about is on a window guard, suspended between heaven and earth. If you do, what you say not only won't be harmful, but it will bring a lot of good to the world.

Driving in the Right Direction

My name is Avishag.

I'm thirteen, and I live in Yerushalayim.

I'm the serious type, maybe a bit too serious. I have a lot of friends—now.

Six months ago, I had tons of social problems. I was always arguing. A girl could be my best friend, but if she did something I didn't like or if she hurt my feelings, I didn't let it pass without a fight. Even if she proved to me that she didn't do it on purpose or that it wasn't what I thought, I still wasn't ready to forgive and forget. Acting this way caused me a lot of social grief.

My story is actually two stories in one. The first part happened six months ago, and it changed me. Then, when the second story happened two weeks ago, I knew I had to tell other kids about it.

My story is about how regular, ordinary people can react when something makes them mad, and how their anger can erupt like a volcano, spewing molten lava on everything in its path.

* * *

First, let me tell you the more recent story, the one that happened two weeks ago.

The scene was a bus stop near my house. It's a very crowded stop, with buses coming and going all the time and lots of people waiting for a bus.

A bus pulled up to the stop, people got on, but the driver didn't pull out right away because a man in a wheelchair wanted to board. The bus behind this one kept honking even though he saw the reason for the delay. When the first bus didn't move, the second one pulled out to pass it. In the process, it scraped the first bus, damaging its mirror. Nothing major, so no problem, right?

Wrong.

Both drivers got out to survey the damage. The driver of the first bus and said to the other bus driver, "You saw I had a disabled passenger. What were you thinking?"

This remark infuriated the second driver.

"I didn't see anything!" he said, and he pushed the first driver.

The driver of the first bus wasn't going to take that sitting down. He responded in kind, and the situation deteriorated until it reached a point where someone called the police. The two bus drivers were arrested, and replacement drivers were called in to continue driving the buses along their routes. I heard that both drivers had their licenses suspended while the incident was investigated and that both risked losing their jobs.

And for what? A scratch on the bus? (My mother says it symbolized the scratch each one felt inside.)

And that's what reminded me of the story that took place six months ago, in the same spot and at almost the exact same time of day.

I was waiting at the bus stop with about another twenty people. One of the people waiting was an elderly man in a wheelchair.

It was hot outside, and people were impatient. The electronic sign said two buses on different routes were due to arrive in another minute. People began moving into place, getting ready to board. The man in the wheelchair positioned himself at the curb.

The first bus arrived, but it was too far from the curb for the driver to lower the wheelchair ramp. He

realized he'd have to back up and pull into the bus stop again. He opened the front passenger door without letting anyone on and called out loudly, "Everyone move back!"

The waiting line of people obeyed the order and moved back, including the man in the wheelchair. The driver began backing up but didn't notice that another bus had just pulled into the stop right behind him.

The driver of the second bus saw what was going on and was about to back up when he saw that a taxi had pulled up right behind him.

The driver of the first bus began backing up. He looked at the crowd on the sidewalk to make sure he wasn't going to hit any of the passengers.

The driver of the second bus leaned on his horn to signal the first bus to stop, but it was too late. We heard a crash.

Someone screamed, and then there was silence. Everyone at the bus stop backed away in panic and pressed themselves against a nearby wall.

Then we saw the damage. The rear window of the first bus had a gaping hole, and glass had flown into the bus. The front end of the second bus was smashed, with its big front windshield one mass of cracks.

The people sitting in the back row of the first bus

must have gotten hit hard by the impact and maybe even injured by the flying glass.

The scene froze for a few seconds. Everyone was in shock. Then people on both buses panicked. Many of them thought it was a terrorist attack. Even those who thought it was "only" an accident were scared.

Then four kids came out of the first bus and told us what had happened.

They'd been sitting at the very back of the bus. When they heard the second bus honking, they turned around to look and saw it was about to crash into their bus. They raced to the front of the bus and were saved.

* * *

"Now what?" all the passengers asked themselves. Surely the two drivers would start to argue about who was to blame. There'd be anger, raised voices, arguments, shouting, and threats. Some people yelled at the driver of the second bus, wanting to know why he hadn't backed up. (They didn't see the taxi right behind him.) But most of the people were mad at the first driver for backing up.

"Who taught you how to drive?" they shouted. "We're going to complain to the company about you!"

Some even went to the driver of the second bus

and offered to serve as witnesses against the driver of the first bus.

By now, both drivers had gotten out of their respective buses and were walking toward each other. I was close enough to see their expressions. To me, it looked like the beginning of a terrible explosion.

The driver of the first bus looked very uncomfortable, as if he knew he was going to get it from the second driver.

And then, the driver of the second bus gave him a big smile.

What was going on? What were they going to do now? Why the big smile?

"Look," said the driver of the first bus, "I—"

"Hold it, my dear brother," the other driver interrupted him. "First, a hug."

He went over to the stunned driver of the first bus and wrapped him in a big bear hug. "Everything's okay," he said, giving him a few pats on the back. "*Baruch Hashem,* no one got hurt. Everything's good. You can relax."

The first driver was still in shock. The crowd gaped in disbelief. Some said, "They must know each other."

"What's your name?" the driver of the second bus said.

MAN

"Yuval," the driver of the first bus answered quietly.

"Nice to meet you. My name is Moshe."

They shook hands.

"Everything's okay. You can relax. We both know no one's to blame for anything. It could only have happened if it was *ratzon Hashem* for it to happen."

"Yeah, but I feel terrible. It was so irresponsible of me. I should have seen that you were right behind me."

"Don't worry about it. No one here is angry with anyone. Brothers don't get angry at each other!"

"Okay, but I still feel so bad. I've been behind the wheel for eight hours today without a break. Traffic jams all over the place. It's terrible that I didn't see you coming."

"Don't get all worked up over it. Relax. We're not to blame at all. Hashem sees everything from Above. He made sure no one was hurt, and He'll continue to help us so that nothing will happen and no one will sue."

"Thanks for not being mad at me," the first driver said. "I mean, I did smash your bus."

"Everything's okay," the second driver said. "I'll explain the situation with the disabled man in the wheelchair. Let's take a few pictures and hope for the best."

Calmly, without any anger, the two drivers photographed the damaged areas of the buses and exchanged contact information.

"Yuval, my brother, let's keep in touch," Moshe said, and then gave him a big hug with a few claps on the back for good measure.

It was a heartwarming moment for all of us there. Everyone felt the *achdus* and how all Jews are brothers.

But that's not the end of the story.

A few months later, my family was in Petach Tikvah for Shabbos for a cousin's bar mitzvah. We stayed with my aunt and uncle.

After candle lighting and davening, I sat on the balcony with my aunt and cousins, talking. We were having fun, and time passed quickly.

Suddenly, something caught my eye. Walking down the street were two fathers and four little boys. The fathers were smiling and talking to each other. The moment came and went, but the scene stayed in my mind.

I've seen them before, the thought flashed through my mind. *That's what it is!*

But I had no idea where.

In the middle of the *seudah,* I remembered. "Wow! It's them!"

You can imagine the looks I got. Like, "What is she talking about?"

It was the two bus drivers from the accident.

"Do you know who those two people are? The ones who walked by while we were sitting on the balcony?" I asked my aunt.

My aunt smiled. "Dozens of people passed our porch tonight."

"They're bus drivers," I said.

"I know of only one bus driver in the neighborhood," she said. "He lives right here in our building, too. His wife is a lovely person. Why do you ask?"

I told her the story.

"That's some story, but I can't say I'm surprised. Our neighbors are wonderful people. I have no idea who the second driver was, but if you'd like, we can go downstairs later and ask what happened next."

After the *seudah,* we knocked on the neighbors' door. A woman opened it and invited us in.

"Shabbat Shalom," my uncle said. "Moshe, there's someone here who says she saw you in a fight with another driver, so I told myself I'd better come over to make sure there won't be any trouble."

Everyone laughed.

"My niece here has a few questions she'd like to

ask you," my uncle said. "Is this a good time? If not, we can come back later."

"Come on in," the woman said. "We just finished eating."

She sat us down on the couch, and I said to her, "I live in Yerushalayim, and we're spending Shabbos here with my aunt and uncle. We were sitting on the balcony when I saw your husband and a friend walking home from shul. I recognized them, but I couldn't remember where I'd seen them. Then it came to me.

"A few months ago, I was waiting at a bus stop in Yerushalayim, and I saw an accident between two buses. Your husband was the driver of one bus. Everyone there was amazed at how your husband hugged the other driver after the accident, and how he was so calm and just wanted to help relax the other driver. People couldn't stop talking about it. But now I saw them walking together and realized that they're friends, so that's probably why he was so nice at the time."

The woman smiled. "They haven't been friends that long. They hadn't even met before the accident.

"I've always known that my husband is a special person, but he never told me the details of this story. From what I know, a week after the accident, they held an investigation and concluded that no one was to blame. Everything was done in a friendly manner, and it all worked out well in the end. And ever since, Moshe and Yuval have been good friends. They even learn together twice a week. Since Yuval has no extended family in the country, we invite him and his wife and children for a Shabbos every so often. We've become like family."

As she was speaking, Yuval's wife joined us and filled in some missing pieces of the puzzle.

Looking at Moshe's wife, she said, "There's something I've never told you before. You've always shown us such warmth, and there's always so much to talk about, that we've never felt the need to share our past. But the truth is, my husband was not always a happy man. He was sad and lonely. He had one good friend, but that was it.

"Two years ago, his friend was seriously injured in an accident. He's still in a coma. It was a big blow to my husband, one from which he still hasn't recovered. He became sad and withdrawn. I saw it happening, but I didn't know how to help him.

"Then, about six months ago, he was in that accident with Moshe. It could have ruined his life. Instead, it was a turning point.

"Moshe could have destroyed him by pressing

charges and proving Yuval was negligent. Instead, Moshe did everything he could to see that Yuval came out of it with a clean record. My husband was bowled over by Moshe's warmth.

"It did something to Yuval. He felt like he'd found a real friend.

"And he had. Moshe turned out to be a great friend. Everything's different for us now. Yuval became a happy person, and his happiness spills over to the whole family. I became friends with you, and our children became friends with yours. It's incredible. That accident could have put my husband out of work, but instead, look where it took us. Sometimes I think the accident was Hashem's way of bringing our two families together."

What made the story extra special for me was that I knew it didn't have to end that way. It could have ended like the first story I told you, where the two drivers fought and lost their jobs. The accident between Moshe and Yuval could have ended the same way: Two drivers. An accident. A big fight. Accusations flying from both sides. And a bad ending.

But these two drivers, Moshe and Yuval, showed me a different way to handle tough situations. It showed me that a smile can go a long way. And that a desire to forgive, to let it go, can turn potential enemies into best friends.

It made me think about the man who wouldn't let Kamtza attend the party he was making.

He could have acted differently. So what if he'd invited Bar Kamtza instead? If he had only welcomed Kamtza with a smile and given in when he pleaded to be allowed to stay, the story would have ended differently. The Beis Hamikdash wouldn't have been destroyed, hundreds of thousands of Jews wouldn't have been slaughtered, and the Jewish people wouldn't have gone into exile and seen their sons and daughters sold into slavery. We wouldn't be in *galus* today, and the Holocaust wouldn't have happened.

Two people. One smile and the world is perfect.

Two people. One bit of hatred, and the world was destroyed.

This story made a huge impact on me. I realized that even if something upsets me, I can try to understand, make up, and forgive.

And you know what? As soon as I decided that, my life changed. I stopped losing friends. Even better, girls I had quarreled with in the past and whose friendship I'd lost came back to me because I made up with them. Now I'm happy and successful socially.

If you're ever in Yerushalayim and take a bus, your driver might be Moshe A. or Yuval M.—and you'll know you've met someone who made the world a better place.

And made me a better person.

The Richest Kid in the World

My name is Eli.

I'm twelve, and I live in Yerushalayim.

There are seven kids in our family. My father works in *chinuch,* and my mother stays at home.

My story is about an issue that many kids will relate to. I'm talking about when we want our parents to buy us things, but they don't agree.

The first time I remember this happening was when I was in first grade. I asked my father to buy me a new bike.

"What's wrong with the one you have?" he said "We bought it for you less than a year ago."

"I know," I said, "but Avi just got a new bike, and I want one too."

Abba sat down next to me and explained that it

doesn't work that way. You don't buy something for a child because his friend got it; you buy it for him if you think he needs it.

"And I think you don't need it, but I'll discuss it with Ima. If she agrees with me, we'll have to say no to your request."

Abba talked it over with Ima. I was hoping Ima would change his mind, but it didn't work out that way. Not only did Ima think the same as Abba, but she came to me and said, "Eli, you have to learn to be happy with what you have. You have a nice bike in good condition. There's no reason to buy you a new bike just because Avi got one."

Five years have passed since then, and I can't even count the number of times I've asked for things and not gotten them.

Don't think my parents don't buy us anything—they do. They've gotten us plenty of toys and games. In fact, a year after that bike request, when I was in second grade, my parents bought me a new bike because Ima said I'd grown, and my bike was too small for me. My parents surprised me with a beautiful new bike, and I was happy as could be. My old bike was passed down to my sister Tali.

I can remember lots of things my parents have

bought my siblings and me over the years, like a computer, a keyboard, a guitar, and of course, clothes and plenty of nosh.

But my story isn't about what I got. It's about what I didn't get.

* * *

As I got older, there were many more times when I asked my parents for something and they told me no. I'm sure it happens to every kid, but I felt it happened to me more than it did to most kids. I had a good reason for feeling that way, too. There were kids in my class who brought all kinds of stuff to class that their parents had gotten them. They bragged about their new bike or the latest computer game or family vacations they'd taken abroad. I'd listen to them, sometimes feeling a little bad and sometimes feeling very bad. I felt that other kids had a lot more than I did.

Whenever I talked about it with my mother, she'd tell me that no one in the world has everything he wants and that even a rich person will always know someone who's richer than he is.

"Look outside. You'll see all kinds of cars driving down the street. Some are cheaper models, others more expensive. Should all the people who own the cheaper

A380

cars feel bad? Does anyone who's not living in a palace need to feel bad because the Queen of England has a palace with over a thousand rooms?"

"But Ima," I said, "I'm not talking about the Queen of England. I'm talking about my friend Avi who's in my class and who I see every day. I'm happy that he has the most expensive shoes and the best ball and that he goes abroad with his family twice a year on vacation and tells me about all the amazing things he does there. But I'd be happy if I also had good shoes, even if they're not the best ones like he has, and if I'd have all the toys and games he has, and if we'd travel abroad every few years. I've never even seen the inside of a plane."

I had tears in my eyes when I said that, and I could see my mother saw how hurt I felt.

Then I asked her, "Ima, are we poor?"

She was shocked. "Poor? Certainly not. How could you say such a thing? Do you know what it means to be poor? A child who's poor doesn't even have chicken for Shabbos. A child who is poor is a child whose parents don't have the money to buy him a winter coat, so he wears an old one that's too small or bundles up in two sweaters that he got from a *tzedakah* organization. A poor child lives in a home where there's no money for heating, so he shivers in the cold.

"You? You eat meat all week long, you have nice clothes and a warm coat, and you have more clothes and toys than a hundred poor children. You're rich, Eli. Remember that. Sure, some children may have more than you do, but that doesn't make you poor."

A few days later, my father took a walk with me. We walked and talked. "Ima and I see that you're feeling a little bitter lately," he said to me. "I hope this conversation will improve your mood.

"The Mishnah asks the question, 'Who is rich?' and answers, 'Someone who is happy with what he has.' Notice that according to this, a person who has no money or clothes or food can be called rich, while a person who has a private plane and a mansion filled with everything you could want can still not be considered rich. How is that possible?"

"How?" I asked.

"Because being rich is not dependent on money or property but on how a person feels," my father said. "If a person feels that things are good for him and that he has enough, he's considered rich. But if he doesn't feel that way, he's considered poor."

I kept quiet. I had something to say, but I didn't dare.

"I know what you're thinking," my father said.

"You're thinking, 'What can I do if I don't feel happy with what I have?'"

That's exactly what I was thinking.

Abba looked at me and said, "We know, Eli. For a while now, we've felt that there are eight rich people in our house and one poor man. The eight rich people are me, Ima, and another six children who are happy with what they have and who feel like the richest people in the world. You can ask them.

"But you, Eli, the second child in the family, are not happy with what you have, and that means we have one child in our family who is poor. For a while, we thought you would outgrow it and that you'd learn to be happy with what you have. When that didn't happen, your mother and I decided to turn you into a rich child."

What a dramatic announcement! I had no idea how my parents were going to make me rich. After all, they weren't rich.

"There are two possibilities for turning you into a rich child," my father said. "One is to buy you everything you ask for, and between you and me, you ask for a lot. But if we do that, your brothers and sisters will think we're playing favorites, and that will cause jealousy in our home. Since the minute a person feels jealous he's no longer happy with what he has, we'll go from having six rich children to six poor children. And the minute we have six poor children, we're all going to be very sad, and it will turn us into parents who aren't happy with what they have. In other words, we'll become poor. And our whole family will change from being a rich family to being a poor family. Would you like to see that happen?"

"No," I said, "I wouldn't."

"Then there's another possibility. We can try to teach you to be happy with what you have and to be rich without buying you things that your siblings aren't getting. Between you and me," my father whispered, "you're getting slightly more than anyone else because you ask for more, yet still that doesn't make you feel rich."

My father was right, and I knew it. I did get more than anyone else because my parents took my needs and wants into consideration. Even though they didn't always think I was right, they gave me more—even if it wasn't everything I'd asked for.

"So how will I become happy with what I have?" I heard myself ask. It didn't seem like there was any way to do that.

Then Abba told me the plan he and Ima had come

up with. It was the strangest, most extraordinary plan I'd ever heard in my life.

"Okay, Eli," my father began, "as we agreed, we can't buy things only for you and not your siblings. If we did, we'd be causing jealousy and sibling rivalry. On the other hand, we want you to be happy with what you have.

"We decided to give you the chance to act like a rich person, by giving you the ability to give to others. We'll begin the journey, and we hope it will give you the feeling of being rich."

Abba told me the whole plan. "We have some savings accounts for future expenses. We've decided to open one account to purchase a few expensive items, such as a new bike and games that most of the boys in your class don't have, plus dozens of new books and CDs. All these things won't be your own private property but will be a public *gemach* for all the kids in the neighborhood. Aside from the children in our family, we won't tell anyone that this is a *gemach*, and we decided that you should run it.

"How will it work? Whenever anyone asks you, you'll have to let him ride a bike or borrow a game, a book, or a CD. As far as the children of the neighborhood are concerned, they will consider it as if you gave it to them. We think it will be good for you. It will make you feel like a rich philanthropist who shares what he has with others. It won't cause jealousy within the family because we'll all know it's a *gemach*. What do you say?"

It sounded good to me. Even better than good. What I liked most was that my parents had thought about me and come up with this amazing idea and were willing to use their savings so I'd be happy with what I have. All that already made me very happy. But I wasn't sure how things would work out.

In the following days, my parents bought a bike and several helmets, special toys and games, books and CDs. They cleared a corner of the basement and put everything there. They didn't advertise a thing—not that there was a *gemach* and not that there was a bike you could take for a ride around the block. They trusted me to take care of all that.

The very first day, I took the bike out and rode around the neighborhood. I got lots of compliments on the new bike, but I was disappointed that no one asked me to let him ride it. I found out later that no one had dared ask me because it never occurred to them that I'd agree to share my expensive new bike.

The second day, the same thing happened. But this time, when a kid asked me about the bike, I asked him,

"Wanna try it?"

"Me? Sure!"

I got off the bike, put the helmet on his head, gave him a few simple instructions on how to use the gears, told him to ride only in safe places, and he was off.

He came back half an hour later with another three kids who got up the courage to say, "Can I have a ride too?"

They almost fainted when they heard me say yes.

Two hours later, I had fifteen kids surrounding me. They all got to ride the bike, and for the first time in my life, I felt like a kid who had everything, and everyone was getting from him. It was an amazing feeling.

Then I told them that I had to go home and casually said, "You know, I've got all sorts of games and books and CDs in our basement. If you feel like it after school, come on over."

From then on, I was busy giving and giving and giving. But it soon started to feel like too much to handle alone, so I asked my brother and sisters to sign up kids for the "library" and the "game room" we'd set up in the basement. We didn't call it a *gemach*; we just had fun sharing what we had with others.

* * *

Two weeks later, Itamar, a new boy who hadn't gotten a turn on the bike, asked me for some help with the gears.

"I don't know much about them," I told him. "Motti here has ridden it a few times and knows how to work them with his eyes closed. He'll tell you all the fancy stuff you can do with it."

Itamar looked at me suspiciously. "I don't get it. Isn't it your bike?"

"It's mine," I said. "You know it's mine."

"If it's your bike, how come Motti knows more about it than you?"

Good question. I thought about it a little, and then I remembered that except for that first day and another few demonstration rides I hadn't ridden the bike at all.

How can it be? I asked myself. *I feel like I've really enjoyed this bike, that it's given me so much pleasure. How is it possible that I've hardly ridden it?*

Suddenly, right at that second, I realized how brilliant my parents' plan for me had been.

For the first time in my life, I felt like a rich kid.

It wasn't the bike. Or the games. It was the feeling.

Who is rich? The person who's happy with what he has. I realized that all my siblings had felt good even before this. But I had needed this experience to teach me that it wasn't the bicycle that made me rich but the good feeling. At that moment, I knew that in the future I wouldn't need a bike or games. I'd just need to work on my emotions to feel as rich as my siblings did.

* * *

Now for the end of the story. Hold on, because you're going to be surprised.

A few months later, something happened in the neighborhood: Avi's father went bankrupt. I didn't know what that meant at first. Then someone explained that it meant he'd had debts so big, he had no way to repay them. To get back some of the money he owed, the bank could take away his house, his car, or any property he owned.

In case you forgot, Avi is the boy in my class I was so jealous of all those years. I'd always felt so poor compared to him.

Avi's family moved from their luxurious mansion to a small rented house. The new situation caused a lot of unpleasantness because they'd always been considered the richest family in the neighborhood, and suddenly they'd become poor.

Abba told me that we all needed to support them and help them live as close as possible to the level they'd lived at before. I didn't get that, so Abba explained.

"Rich people," he told me, "are at a disadvantage in a certain way. They get used to living at the top, and if that level is taken away from them, they suffer much more than other people. That's why there's a mitzvah in the Torah to help rich people who have lost their money even more than ordinary poor people."

* * *

One day Avi came down to the basement and asked if he could take the bike.

It was a sad moment. Avi, whom I had always envied, didn't even own a bike. I gave him the bike, and he left.

After he left, I wondered if I could help him in some way. Suddenly I realized that I could. I knew just what would work because only a few months earlier I had felt like he did now, poor. Thanks to my parents, though, I'd found a way to feel rich. And that gave me an idea.

When he came to return the bike, I said to him, "Avi, listen to this. You know that bike belongs half to me and half to the whole neighborhood. I'm pretty busy with the books and CDs now. Would you mind taking charge of the bike and lending it out to other kids? You know, showing them how the gears work and stuff?"

Avi's eyes sparkled. "Sure thing!"

"Just remember, you get the most fun not by riding the bike but by giving it out to other kids."

"I know," he said. "You don't know how jealous I was when everyone came to ask you for the bike. Don't worry. I'm going to do a great job."

Avi took the bike, glowing with happiness.

I went back inside the house and told my parents what had just happened. You wouldn't believe how happy they were. They hugged me and kissed me and praised me for what I'd done.

When I went to sleep that night, I thought about all the recent developments: about the long way and the short way from poor to rich and from feeling jealous of another person to feeling unbelievably happy with what I have.

And then I fell asleep, feeling like the richest kid in the world.

Thunder in the Classroom

My name is Naomi.

I'm thirteen, and I live in Yerushalayim.

I couldn't decide whether or not to send in this story because it's about a situation that I don't think most kids will run into. Still, I thought it might be useful for those who do, so here goes.

I'm a happy, popular girl, and what you'd call a born optimist. I've always liked going to school—seeing my friends, playing games at recess, laughing a lot, and, of course, learning. I never get into fights or arguments. I tend to smile at life, and life tends to smile back at me.

Over the past few months, I ran into a serious problem. Some girls in my class—even those I'd been close with, and even my best friend—started keeping their distance. I tried everything I could think of to change it, but nothing worked.

At a certain point, I decided to talk to my parents about it. And no, it wasn't easy. They're always so happy and proud that I'm a popular girl. How could I disappoint them by telling them what was going on?

But in our family, we don't keep things bottled up inside. My parents don't think it's healthy. So I went to my parents and said, "Something's going on in my class. I don't know exactly what it is, but it feels like girls are cutting me off."

My parents gave me their full attention and wanted to hear more. They promised not to talk to anyone about it without my consent.

I didn't know where to start, so they asked me questions, trying to get the full picture. They said it wasn't *lashon hara* for me to tell them because you tell your parents everything.

I told them it had all started with a fight between two girls who'd been best friends for years: Malky and Tali. Tali became friends with a third girl, who kept putting down Malky. The friendship broke up.

Malky was a good friend of mine. And because of that, I was being rejected too.

My parents took a pen and paper and started

writing down who was friends with whom and who'd fought with whom. I saw something interesting: Most of the girls who'd been friends in recent years were no longer friends, and all of them had become friends with one girl.

Baila.

The more I talked to my parents, the more I realized that the person who got everyone to go against us was Baila.

"You know something? That name sounds familiar," my mother said.

My father and I gave her a puzzled look.

"I remember now," my mother said. "She was moved into your class in fifth grade, right?"

"She was! How do you remember?"

"I remember...because your father and I tried to prevent it."

* * *

My cousin Nechama's mother had told my mother that Baila had gotten her daughter's class riled up. She'd caused hatred and fighting, even hitting. She'd bullied so many girls that a few parents complained to the school and said, "It's either her or us."

The administration had no choice. They told Baila's

parents that she would be transferred to the parallel class and warned them that she had to change her behavior.

When my mother found out that Baila would be joining my class, she'd wanted to go straight to the principal and protest. She thought that a group of parents going together would be most effective. Nechama's mother had said to her, "I've never seen anything like it. She sets the classroom on fire to the point that even now, after she left, we're having a hard time putting out the flames."

My father, who works in *chinuch,* thought they shouldn't say anything yet.

"Let's give the girl a chance," he'd told my mother. "She's gotten a blow, because now she has to switch classes, leaving all her friends behind. She's probably learned her lesson. Now's the best time to give her an opportunity to improve."

My father also called Baila's parents and suggested they keep a close eye on their daughter to help her succeed. On the flip side, he told them, "I'm going to ask my daughter to befriend her and invite her to our home."

* * *

Now I remembered that I *had* invited Baila to our house. It happened after she began calling me up, giggling, and then hanging up. At first, I thought it was a joke, but when my mother and father and the home phone began getting these annoying calls about fifty times a day, I told my parents that I knew who was calling. I said she was someone who had been in my cousin Nechama's class and had transferred to mine.

I recalled asking my cousin Nechama, when Baila transferred from her class to ours, "How's Baila?"

"Um, she's okay."

Which meant she wasn't. "Tell me."

She hadn't replied. She's careful not to talk about other people, and I am too. My curiosity had made me ask, but I dropped the subject when I realized it was *lashon hara*.

My mother called her sister, Nechama's mother. I don't know what they said to each other, but after that conversation, my mother told me, "I'd like you to befriend Baila. She needs friends."

I thought it was strange that my mother was telling me to be friends with someone who was harassing us on the phone, but when my parents tell me to do something, I do it.

The harassment stopped.

I felt that Baila was jealous of me and was taking it out on me, but I didn't pay much attention to it. To me, she was a girl with no self-esteem. My parents had asked me to be nice to her, and I was.

* * *

At first, Baila didn't have much success arousing animosity in our class. Mostly, we all felt sorry for her. But without us realizing it, she managed to separate Riki from Shani, who were not only neighbors but best friends. Their separation shocked the class because it came along with so much hatred and slander.

Baila was never mentioned as the cause of the split. Riki and Shani accused each other of disloyalty, of talking behind the other's back. Their fight created a bad atmosphere in the class.

Then, another pair of friends, Shifra and Dassy, and another trio, Toby, Penina, and Yaeli quarreled. We didn't connect the situations, and for some reason, we didn't connect it with Baila. She was still considered an object of pity, a girl we were supposed to be nice to, which we all tried our best to do.

I was friends with everyone, but my best friend was Tehilla. I had another few close friends and got along with every girl in the class.

But then the animosity spread to our group. Two of my closest friends began to quarrel and to talk negatively about each other. They ended up fighting. Then it reached me—or, to be more accurate, my friend Tehilla. Within a few days, rumors spread that Tehilla was talking against other girls and had formed a group to plan a *cherem*. It was all lies, but most of the class believed it.

I only realized how serious things were when our homeroom teacher called in Tehilla to reprimand her. She said girls had complained that Tehilla was acting snobby to them and was talking about them behind their backs. "You're causing trouble in the class, and I won't stand for it," the teacher told her.

Tehilla couldn't believe it. She denied all the accusations, but the teacher didn't believe her.

"I've gotten reports from many girls about things you've said. Are you claiming that it's a conspiracy?"

Tehilla thought a little, and then said, "I didn't say anything about anyone. I'm very careful not to talk *lashon hara*, and I have no idea why they said I did."

The teacher pursed her lips. "When so many girls complain, I have a responsibility to act. This is my first and last warning."

When Tehilla came to tell me about it, she was

crying. We were both totally shocked because we knew it wasn't true. Someone was feeding the teacher lies!

A few days later, the principal called in Tehilla's parents for a meeting. She warned them that if Tehilla didn't shape up fast, she, the principal, would be forced to take drastic measures. Tehilla's parents were refined people with great respect for authority, and they promised the principal that they would do as she asked. They came home and told Tehilla that they were very disappointed in her.

Tehilla was hurt. "Do you think I would do something like that?"

"No, but the principal doesn't make things up. We also heard that she spoke to you about this issue several days ago. Why didn't you tell us?"

Tehilla didn't know what to say. She burst into tears and ran to her room to call me.

That's when I decided to tell my parents everything.

* * *

My parents took it very seriously.

Over the next few days, I heard my parents on the phone with the parents of other girls in my class and the parallel class.

Meanwhile, the situation in our class deteriorated.

Tehilla and I were given the cold shoulder; nobody spoke to us.

"Too bad you're Tehilla's friend," a few girls told me privately. "We like you, but we can't be friends with you if you're friends with that girl."

That's what they called Tehilla: "that girl."

"What's the problem?" I asked them.

They told me all sorts of things that I knew weren't true. For instance, they said that Tehilla had called a meeting to get girls to exclude other girls from the group. They even "knew" the exact date and time that this so-called meeting had taken place. I tried telling them that Tehilla had been at my house then, and besides, she was very careful not to speak *lashon hara*.

"So she's caught you in her net too, huh? You're taking her side? Too bad!"

It was a nightmare. Where had this whole thing come from?

After I told my parents about it, they said, "Don't worry. We'll take care of it."

* * *

One day my parents told me, "There's going to be a meeting at school. We want you to come and tell the whole story."

They told me about the talks they'd had in recent days. They explained that I was up against a problem I wasn't expected to know how to deal with, a problem that a girl my age shouldn't even know existed.

"One in a thousand people has a problem like this, where she has no inner peace and tries to stir up trouble all the time. When such a person enters a new workplace, for instance, even mature, respected people can suddenly find themselves pitted against each other, fighting and arguing. They'll never blame the person who's causing it because they don't realize that her hidden anger is what stirred up the animosity."

The meeting was set for the evening, when the school was empty. I was excited about it because it meant the adults were taking this seriously and they'd try to find a solution.

When we got there, I met a girl from the parallel class who was there with her parents. Besides us, the principal, the assistant principal, our homeroom teacher, the school psychologist, and the parents of one of my classmates attended the meeting.

The father of the girl in the parallel class began by saying that he felt very bad about having this meeting because he knew that on the other side was a girl who needed help. But the first help we needed to give her was to get her to stop doing what she was doing because it was destroying the lives of seventy girls, one of them his daughter.

He asked his daughter Sari to describe what she and her friends had suffered through since third grade, the year Baila had joined their class.

Sari talked about how she'd been separated from all her friends, and how a situation was created in which several groups of girls fought with each other, turning the classroom into a jungle. She also drew a map of the classroom dynamics before Baila entered the class and another one showing what it looked like two years later. What a difference! A unified class had been torn to shreds.

Her ending was even more impressive. She said it took a year to heal all the rifts and conflicts, and that now, finally, the class had *achdus* again and was fun to be in. Her parents explained how all the parents of girls in that class had banded together to have Baila transferred to a parallel class and how good it had been for the girls.

Then my father asked me to speak. He promised that nothing I said would leave the room and that it was for a beneficial purpose.

I described the unity our classroom once had. I

made a map of the classroom dynamics that showed all the friendships and how everyone had gotten along with everyone. And then I drew a diagram of the current situation, where all the friendships had broken apart, and everyone in Baila's group was against me and my friend Tehilla. Then I added, "It's only now that the focus is on us. The minute she has us isolated and our status is reduced to zero, she'll work on someone else. She's very powerful."

Our teacher was shocked.

"It sounds very strange to me," she said. "Baila seems so weak and helpless."

"She seems that way," I said. "But she uses her weakness to her advantage. It works like this: a girl feels sorry for her and tries to be her friend. When Baila feels close enough, she'll casually drop a few hurtful comments that cause animosity. For instance, she'll say, 'So-and-so (the girl's best friend) says she's glad she's not short like you, but I don't think you're that short at all.' Stuff like that."

I gave more examples of things Baila had said to me and added, "I'm pretty sure she's done this to other girls as well."

I finished saying what I had to say, and my father repeated what he had explained to me: that he thought

ואהבת
Devra

Baila wasn't a bad girl but a girl with a serious personality disorder, a rare case of a child who caused grief to those around her. He told the school staff not to blame themselves for not seeing the whole picture because such cases are rare, and when they do occur, even smart, sophisticated people can find themselves embroiled in arguments with one another.

"For years you've thought that you were dealing with a poor little girl who needed your protection. All I've done tonight is try to show you the other side of the story. I don't usually get involved in my children's social issues, but I think this situation is impossible for my daughter to cope with on her own. I also don't want her to learn how to deal with such a serious problem because I much prefer that my daughter remains in the innocent world of normalcy.

"I know that if my daughter had ended her friendship with Tehilla," my father added, "she could have avoided all this. But I want my daughter to know that you don't abandon a friend when the going gets tough. You stick up for your friends even if it might mean some sacrifice. Now I leave things in your competent hands."

* * *

Wow.

What a great feeling to see how my parents protected me! I told myself that even if things didn't work out, at least I knew I had parents who believed in me. I also knew that even if I didn't have a single friend right now, at least I'd done the right thing, and nothing was my fault. Just knowing that I was okay, that I hadn't done anything wrong but had just encountered a girl with a problematic personality, made me feel a whole lot better.

Everything worked out a lot faster than I expected.

Baila was suspended. The principal, teachers, school psychologist, and other professionals they brought in spoke with every single girl in our class. Within a short time, they were able to explain to all of us exactly what had happened. All the broken friendships were restored, and girls began to realize that someone had gotten between them, lit a fire of *lashon hara* and *rechilus*, and made up things that had never, ever happened—or repeated things that had been said but twisted them. Baila had exposed each of our weak spots, creating two things: conflict and weakness. It's called "divide and conquer."

* * *

Baila returned to class two weeks later. We were told to welcome her and not to exclude her, but on the other hand, they gave us ways to protect ourselves from *lashon hara* and *rechilus*. The main strategy was that if Baila began to say something that could cause an argument, we shouldn't listen. I think the staff did an amazing job of preparing us because Baila didn't even try.

Peace and quiet returned to our class, and each of us learned a lesson we'll never forget.

* * *

I hope you never encounter such a case, but if it happened to me, I guess it could happen to others as well. If you feel that suddenly people are speaking *lashon hara* and *rechilus*, that there are conflicts and quarrels, tell your parents or a teacher. The instigator is usually one girl or boy with the power to cause animosity, to weaken others in order to make themselves more powerful. In other words, to divide and conquer.

If such children don't get the right treatment, they'll grow up to cause destruction wherever they go, whether in high school or yeshivah. Even after they're married, their relationships will be complicated and problematic. But if it's caught in time, they can be helped.

This story is worth it if it helps even one kid who finds himself in a situation where everyone's against him, and he doesn't know what's happening. But I'm adding a warning: Don't try to handle it by yourself. Tell your parents or a teacher. If talking about it is hard for you, show them this story. Tell them that similar things are happening to you. They'll check things out and decide what to do.

During Sefiras HaOmer, all the *talmidim* of Rabbi Akiva died because they didn't respect each other enough. After this happened to me, I wondered if it wasn't all started by one student.

Before you read this story, you wouldn't have known what I meant by that. Now you do.

"And Leave the Driving to...
Yehudit!"

My name is Yehudit.

I'm twelve, and I live in a small village in Eretz Yisrael.

A little while ago, I drove, and not just a car, but a school bus. And not just a school bus, but one filled with kids. It lasted only a little while, but it's a fact: I drove.

Before you jump to conclusions, let me tell you how it happened.

My sisters and I, along with the rest of the kids in our village, are bused to school. The driver we get on any particular day is never happy about having to drive us. You know how it is. Kids get excited, they shout, and he needs to drive.

This year, the bus company gave us a new driver named Benny. This story is about him.

Benny seemed to like driving us, and I guess the bus company was happy to have finally found the right driver because he became our regular driver.

One Friday when school was let out, my sisters and I left the building and walked across the street to the bus. When we got there, the bus door was closed. I looked inside and saw that the driver was sleeping. I called out to him, but he didn't move. I pulled hard on the door handle, and the door opened. My sisters and I climbed onto the bus.

Soon the rest of the kids boarded the bus, too. The radio was blaring, and everyone started acting wild, but the driver kept on sleeping.

I walked to the front of the bus and noticed a half-chewed piece of gum, still wet, on the driver's shirt. I looked back at the seats and saw that everyone who usually rode the bus was there. Once they were all settled in their seats, I tried to wake up the driver so he could start the route. I called his name a few times, each time louder, but he didn't wake up.

Things were getting out of hand. Kids were singing and dancing and fooling around, but Benny still didn't wake up.

Then a girl who was running away from another girl banged into the driver's seat. Benny opened his eyes, looking dazed.

I breathed a sigh of relief. "Good morning!" I said. "We're right in front of the school, and everyone's here, so can we can start the ride home?"

Benny ignored me.

"Can you please drive us home?"

He tapped on his phone as if he was going to make a call…and then stopped.

"It's time to go home," I tried again. "We need to go."

Benny tapped on his phone again.

I didn't know what to do.

"Uh, I need to call my mother," I said as I took his phone.

He didn't protest.

"Ima, the driver doesn't want to drive us home!" I shouted when I reached my mother. "We've been sitting here in the bus for ten minutes. We all want to go home, but the driver doesn't want to drive!"

We didn't think anything was wrong. We just thought Benny was being stubborn.

My mother called the bus company. Meanwhile, I opened the bus door and went outside to talk to a teacher I saw standing there. I explained the problem. By the time she understood me and tried to help, the bus almost drove off without me. While I was talking to the teacher, the other kids had asked the driver to take them home. Right at the worst moment for me, the bus began moving forward. I ran after it, shouting, "Stop!"

By now, it dawned on me that something must be wrong with Benny. He wasn't acting normal.

The bus screeched to a stop, sending all the kids flying.

As I quickly got on the bus, the teacher I'd been talking with called out, "Yehudit, your job is to make sure everyone is sitting in their seat."

I asked everyone to sit down and buckle up.

At that moment—when the cell phone started ringing, kids were acting wild, and I was standing there wondering what was going on—Benny stepped on the gas. The bus raced ahead so fast that one wheel even climbed up on the curb.

Worse of all, Benny was driving in the wrong direction.

The cell phone was ringing in Benny's hand, but he wasn't answering. I took it and pressed answer.

It was the manager of the bus company.

I spoke fast. "Hello, I'm the girl in charge. The driver didn't want to take us home, but now he decided that he would, but he's going in the wrong direction! We keep telling him he's going the wrong way, but it looks like he doesn't even know where he is!"

"Ask the driver to pull over to the side of the road," the manager said.

"Pull over to the side!" I shouted to the driver.

The first and second graders started to scream in terror. The older kids were also scared stiff.

But instead of pulling over to the side, Benny kept going. It looked like we'd crash into the garbage truck in front of us! We were on a two-lane road, and Benny tried to pass by going into the lane for oncoming traffic. He turned the wheel slightly to move into the opposite lane, but the bus didn't move out far enough. I noticed that he didn't seem to have a tight grip on the steering wheel, either, like most drivers do. If he didn't turn the wheel more, we'd crash right into the garbage truck!

I grabbed the steering wheel and turned it to the left. Our bus passed the garbage truck safely, but suddenly I saw a car coming straight at us.

"Stop!" I shouted to Benny.

He hit the brakes so suddenly I almost fell.

But now, instead of the bus pulling over to the side,

we were stopped smack in the middle of the road. Cars came toward us, and people shouted at Benny that he was blocking the road, but he didn't move.

One of the people our bus was blocking got out of his car and looked inside the bus. He saw children screaming, jumping up and down, and crying hysterically. He didn't know what was going on.

"Everyone sit back down in your seat immediately!" he shouted. "I don't want to see a single child out of his seat. Your wild behavior is preventing the poor driver from driving!"

I knew the problem wasn't with us kids but with the driver.

Cars moved, and our driver got back into the right lane with a little help from me on the steering wheel. At my insistence, he stayed close to the right shoulder. I continued to turn the steering wheel as best I could while asking him to please slow down and stop when he saw a place to park. He didn't seem to understand me, because he parked in the middle of the road again. By now, I knew how to get through to him. It was almost like talking to a baby.

"Come on," I cajoled. "Push down on the gas pedal just a tiny drop harder."

He stepped on the gas lightly.

"Turn right—here! Here! Okay, now stop!" I put out my hand to signal a stop.

I was confused. I called my mother again, but she didn't answer. I called my father, and he said he'd try to find out what was happening and notify the other parents.

I knew something had happened to the driver, but I had no idea what.

And then a realization struck me. Benny was obeying my commands, but I couldn't count on him to drive the bus anymore. Something was happening to him, and I didn't know what it was. But whatever it was, a flash of sudden insight told me it was no longer safe for any of us to stay on the bus.

"Now stop and open the door," I said.

Benny obeyed.

I think that was the most important decision I'd ever made in the entire twelve years of my life.

I turned around to face the other kids on the bus. "Everyone get off the bus and stand by that big tree. Put your backpacks down and wait quietly."

And then I did something that only Hashem could have guided me to do. I turned the key in the ignition and shut the engine.

Benny said, "Key, phone—give it to me and let's go."

I stuffed the keys deep in my backpack.

I left the bus and went over to the group clustered around the tree. I made sure the younger girls had water, and everyone started saying *tehillim*. I took two of the older girls back with me to the bus and told them their job was to watch the driver and make sure the door stayed open.

I sat down on one of the seats and used Benny's phone. The bus company said they were sending a different bus and that it should get there very soon. My mother called to make sure everything was okay.

Every time I checked on Benny, he mumbled something that sounded like, "I have another trip to make. I need the phone…the phone."

I knew I couldn't let him drive. I thought he was drunk or something. Besides, I needed his phone.

"When can I leave?" he demanded.

"Don't worry," I said. "The company said your job is to stay here now. Don't move from here."

Every time he looked like he wanted to start driving, the three of us shouted, "Stop!"

It worked.

Finally, the replacement bus arrived. I gave the phone back to Benny and got off the bus.

We all boarded the other bus and found seats.

MAN

Some girls were still crying. We put on relaxing music, and things settled down. The ride went by pleasantly, *baruch Hashem*.

* * *

Meanwhile, the mystery was solved. The police arrived and ordered an ambulance for Benny. The paramedics said it looked like he'd had a stroke. Benny wasn't drunk, and he hadn't decided to act crazy all of a sudden. He'd just had a cerebral hemorrhage, which made him act the way he did. It wasn't his fault at all.

My parents started getting tons of phone calls praising me for the way I'd acted.

My mother hugged and kissed me, and that's when I realized what a miracle I'd experienced. If I hadn't noticed that something was a little bit off, *chas v'shalom*, or if I hadn't realized there was anything wrong with the driver's behavior, the story could have had a tragic ending. I don't even want to think about how a busload of kids, me included, was racing down the highway in a bus out of control.

A few days after it happened, the owner of the bus company called my father to commend me for my quick thinking and to express his appreciation for the way I handled the situation.

After we recovered, we decided to make a *seudas hodayah* in shul to express our thanks to Hashem for saving us from an accident.

* * *

I learned from this story how important it is to pay attention to what's going on and to take action when something doesn't seem right.

Another thing I learned from this story is that an adult can't always see what a child is seeing. One driver stopped and saw what was going on, but he came to the wrong conclusion. He thought the driver had stopped because the kids were acting up, which, to him, made sense. It didn't occur to him that the bus driver was the problem.

We kids have a role too. When something seems wrong to us, we can't assume that everything's okay. If something doesn't make sense to us, we need to do something. And that something is to call our parents or another adult we trust and ask them what to do.

This is true not only when a driver has a stroke, but in every situation where we encounter strange, abnormal behavior—even if the person is an adult and even if that person is someone we trust and love.

When behavior appears not normal to us, it

probably isn't, and we need to tell someone and do something about it so it doesn't continue. That's what I learned, and if other kids learn that from my story, then it was worth it for me to tell it.

Noam's Story

My name is Noam.

I'm twelve, and I live in Sderot.

In case you think Sderot is some ordinary town somewhere in Eretz Yisrael, let me tell you where it's located.

It's on the border of Gaza.

Which means living in fear of rockets and warning sirens and terrorists sneaking in through tunnels.

I've got two stories to tell you. It might not seem like there's a connection between them, but once you've read them both, you'll see the connection.

My first story took place at the beginning of summer vacation. Our camp took us on a trip up north. It was one of the best trips I've ever been on. We had a blast. We hiked, sang, and just broke loose from a year's worth of stress from fire kites, rockets, and warning sirens.

On the last day of our trip, we boarded the bus and headed for Menara Cliff. Three days of nonstop fun and just about zero sleep had turned us into zombies. I sprawled out on a back seat and was out like a light.

When we arrived at our destination, everyone got off the bus.

Everyone but me.

It wasn't a decision. It's just that I was sound asleep. I didn't dream that I was about to live through the worst nightmare of my life.

I guess no one saw me back there. My friends were as sleep deprived as I was. They probably just shuffled to the door blindly and left. I guess the driver closed the doors and left the bus without making the security rounds as he was supposed to.

At some point, I woke up. I remember wondering why it was so quiet, and then I drifted off again. When I woke up a second time, I remembered that my name was Noam and that I was at camp, and that the last time I'd been awake I'd been irritated by all the noise my friends were making when I was trying to sleep. Now the silence was oppressive.

Where was everyone?

I stood up. The bus was empty. I figured the driver was resting in one of the seats.

I walked through the bus, checking seats. As I neared the front, a few things dawned on me: I was alone on the bus; even the driver wasn't there. The doors were closed, and I had no way of opening them. It was boiling hot, and there wasn't too much air in the bus.

I banged on a window as hard as I could. Nothing happened except that my hand hurt. The glass was so strong, I didn't even make any noise.

I looked outside. I was surrounded by a sea of empty buses and cars. Even if someone had been inside them, he wouldn't have heard me.

I tried to open a window, but it didn't open. None of them did. That's the kind of windows they were—just pieces of glass set into place. The only air circulating in the bus came from the air conditioner, but it was off. It was so hot and stuffy in there, I felt like I was suffocating.

I walked up and down the aisle nervously, trying to think of what to do. I had no way of contacting anyone. I walked back to the driver's seat and saw through the front windshield a family loading things into the

trunk of their car. I started yelling and shouting and pounding on the glass, but they didn't even turn their heads.

I watched helplessly as they got into their car and drove off.

I tried opening the bus door, but it wouldn't budge. I'd heard plenty of stories about kids who were left inside a vehicle and died. I never thought it would happen to me.

Except that it was.

After trying all my options, I went back to the driver's seat for the third time and decided to search for a heavy object I could use to break a window and escape.

Suddenly, I saw a cell phone. I picked it up to call my mother and tell her what was going on.

I pressed the button to turn on the phone.

Nothing happened. The battery must have died.

Tears of frustration filled my eyes, but I didn't give up. I looked around for a cable to charge the phone and found one. I plugged the phone into one of the holes I saw. I worked calmly and quickly because I didn't want to waste any time. It was getting harder to breathe.

I heard a beep. The phone was charging.

I waited a minute and then pressed the "on" button

again. The cell phone slowly came to life. The screen said, "Enter Code."

I almost screamed. How was I supposed to know the code?

I was just about ready to give up, but then I remembered...

My mother once told me that every cell phone will let you make an emergency call even if you can't unlock it. (Now you know it too. Pass it on.) This information saved my life. I searched the screen for the word "emergency" and pressed it. Now I could see the keypad. I tapped in the number 100 for the police, and then pressed the "call" button. (That's the number here in Israel. In the US, the emergency number is 911.)

A policewoman answered. I told her my name and how old I was, just like I told you at the beginning of the story. Then I told her I was stuck inside a locked bus. I tried to speak clearly despite feeling scared.

She asked me where I was located.

"I don't know," I said.

"Tell me what you see," she said.

"I see a sign saying, 'Galilee Chicken.'"

She told me that she needed more information. I looked around, but aside from the buses surrounding me on all sides, all I saw was trees. Then I noticed the bus company's name and phone number and told it to her.

"Good going," she said. "Stay on the line with me while I get to work."

By now I was suffocating. I felt very hot, like I was burning up. I realized that this was what all those children must have felt like just before...

I didn't want to think about it.

I said to the policewoman in a quiet voice, "Can you please find someone fast? Because I really don't feel good."

"You're a smart boy and a brave one too. Hang in there just a few more minutes."

I was relieved that at least someone knew I was trapped in the bus. But I hoped she'd get someone to come before anything happened to me.

And then I heard a siren, and I knew my troubles were over.

A fire truck pulled up and drove around among the buses, searching for the one I was in. I banged on the window and waved my arms. Finally, the driver looked in my direction. When he saw me, he zoomed over. I could barely hear him through the window as he shouted to me, "We'll get you out in a couple of minutes. Don't worry!"

They took out equipment and began banging on the door. After about a minute, the door flew open and air rushed in. I tumbled out and collapsed on the sidewalk. Then I just lay there, exhausted, all red and sweaty.

A police patrol car pulled up.

The policemen brought me into their air-conditioned car. They gave me water and told me to sip it slowly. They asked me how I was feeling, plus a whole lot of other questions.

Then an ambulance arrived. The paramedics helped me climb up into it, and then they examined me. They checked my blood pressure and temperature and all kinds of things. Gradually, I returned to my normal self. When they saw I was okay, they contacted the camp director.

The fire truck drove away, but not before the firefighters asked me how I was feeling and told me I was a real hero and had shown true courage. They said that if I ever wanted to be a firefighter, I'd be welcomed to their company with open arms.

The police asked me lots of questions. When they were finished, I said to them, "If it's okay with you, I'd like to go back to camp because I don't want to miss seeing Menara Cliff." (I told them that because I felt bad for the camp director. With all due respect to Menara Cliff, the last thing I needed right then was an exciting adventure.)

* * *

That was the first story. The point, to me anyway, is don't lose your cool. If you find yourself in a tough spot, don't give up. And remember the emergency option on a cell phone. (Make sure you don't dial it as a prank. A prank call to an emergency number might take the police or an ambulance away from people who need them. Not only that, but making a prank call is a crime and goes on a person's record for life.)

I thought that was the end of it. But the second story, which happened less than a week later, put a whole new spin on the first one.

As you probably know, the security situation in Sderot is tense. We live less than a mile from the Gaza Strip, so rockets and fire kites are a routine part of our lives.

A few days after I got locked in the bus, my mother suggested that we go to a nearby attraction for some fun and relaxation. There's a kibbutz not far from us that raises dogs for sale and allows people to play with them. It's sort of like a petting zoo with dogs. We took my cousin Eviatar and his little sister Tzofia, who's nine. They live in Sderot too.

I entered a cage with a lot of dogs in it. They jumped on me from all directions, ready to play. I was having fun enjoying the dogs, when all of a sudden, we heard a loud boom. My mother asked the person in charge, "What was that?"

"Don't worry," he said. "It's probably the army."

We relaxed, but then we turned around to look and saw smoke filling the entrance.

We've seen a lot of smoke in our area. You wouldn't believe the damage those kites are doing. But I'd never had one land so close to me. Usually, they land in an open field and set it on fire. This time, the kite set the dog kennel on fire.

We raced for the exit, but it was filled with smoke. I was surprised to see how fast fire moves. It took only a few seconds for all of us—adults, kids, and dogs—to be in danger. Fire and smoke were everywhere, and we didn't know what to do. Meanwhile, the man in charge released all the dogs, and most of them ran for their lives.

We got into the car and started driving away.

"Give me the phone," I said to my mother.

"When we get home," she said.

"Please," I insisted. "I have to call the emergency number."

My mother handed me her cell phone, and I called the fire department to report the fire.

The firefighters arrived within minutes.

We drove into the kibbutz, with my mother honking and telling everyone to go help put out the fire. Then we went back and watched as rescue workers battled the blaze. We took pictures and were the first to spot a new fire that broke out in a place where the firefighters couldn't see it.

I ran with my cousin Eviatar to tell the firefighters about it.

All of a sudden, two policemen came over to us and asked, "Who's the boy who called?"

My mother pointed to me.

"Do you know that you're the only one who called?" one of the policemen said to me.

Everyone had been in such a panic, so busy trying to get away, that they hadn't thought to call. *Baruch Hashem,* my call saved the day.

Then one of the firefighters said to me, "What's your name, sonny?"

"Noam," I replied.

"Would you like to be a firefighter?" he asked me.

I grinned. "That's the second offer I've gotten this week. I'll think about it."

"The second offer? How's that?"

My mother told him a shortened version of my first story, and the two policemen and the firefighters tipped their hats to me (really!) and said, "If only every kid were like you."

I think everything that happened to me was *min haShamayim*.

The first story forced me to find a way to solve my personal problem, and I feel that Hashem gave me that experience so that when the dog kennel went up in flames, I could help save all the visitors and the dogs.

I grew from both of those experiences. They turned me into a determined boy who will always choose to take action rather than give up.

I hope none of you will ever be put to the test like I was, but if you are, face it bravely. Take action, and with Hashem's help, you'll succeed.

Just like I did.

The Afikoman Inside Me

My name is Tzippy.

I'm twelve, and I live in Telz-Stone.

We usually celebrate the Pesach Seder with my grandparents. Every year we switch off going to my father's parents and my mother's parents. Both sets of grandparents live in Yerushalayim.

At the home of my Zeidy Schwartz, my father's father, Seder night is pretty much the same as it is in every Jewish home. Zeidy hides the afikoman when no one's looking, and then we search for it. If we can't find it, he'll give us hints for where to look. Whoever finds it bargains with Zeidy to see how much he's willing to "pay" to get it back.

With my mother's father, Zeidy Weiss, things are completely different.

First of all, Zeidy Weiss always hides the afikoman in such a secret place that we've never been able to find it. To find it, we have to solve a series of riddles. One riddle leads to the next, and this goes on throughout the whole Seder. It's sort of a treasure hunt with all the grandchildren working as a team. In the end, we don't "steal" the afikoman; it's given to us.

Afterward, we negotiate to see how much solving all the riddles is worth. The negotiations aren't conducted with Zeidy Weiss (who says he's the worst businessman he knows) but with Bubby Weiss, who's considered a successful businesswoman.

The gifts are always special, or as Bubby Weiss likes to say, "tailor-made for the recipient." It might be a new pair of glasses, clothing, or a book (always Bubby's first choice), or even a trip with Zeidy and Bubby.

Another thing: We don't get the gifts on Seder night but a few days later. Zeidy and Bubby say it's always better to think a little before making a decision.

* * *

Last year on *chol hamoed* Pesach, when we were still at my grandparents' house, Bubby said she wanted to talk to me.

I knew it must have something to do with the afikoman we won. (Don't you agree that sounds better than "stole"?)

I was right.

"Tzippy, have you given some thought to what you want for your afikoman present?" Bubby asked me.

"Yes," I said. "I want to go with you and Zeidy on your next vacation." My grandparents usually take two grandchildren with them on their vacation, and this year I hoped one of them would be me.

"That sounds reasonable," Bubby said. "But I have an even more tempting offer for you."

It sounded good already.

"As you know, we usually vacation right here in Eretz Yisrael. We'll be doing that this year too, but in addition, we plan to travel abroad this summer. The question is, would you like to join us on our vacation here or would you rather wait and come with us when we go to Europe?"

My heart beat faster. "Of course I want to go to Europe!"

"Okay," Bubby said, "but the trip comes with a price."

I figured Bubby might ask me to come over to help her once a week (which I'd gladly do anyway, even without the promise of a trip). What she said next took me by surprise.

"What I want to ask you to do, Tzippy, doesn't involve me or anyone else. Only you."

I didn't say anything. I wondered what she had in mind.

When Bubby didn't continue right away, I knew that whatever she said would be serious.

"Look, Tzippy," she began carefully, "you know that your mother and I talk about you grandchildren. I'm interested in your health, how you're doing in school, how it's going for you socially."

I felt my cheeks burn. It wasn't a subject I felt like discussing. I felt a flare of anger at my mother for discussing it with Bubby. I'd rather Bubby didn't know I had any social problems. I wished my mother didn't know either, but I can't hide anything from her. I guess if she knew that meant Bubby would know too.

I was wrong.

"Tzippy, if you prefer not to talk about it with me, I'll stop right now," Bubby said. "Your mother didn't tell me anything, and she wasn't the one who raised the subject. I asked her because I sensed something. At first, she didn't reply, but then she told me I could talk to you about it if I wanted. That was the extent of our

conversation on this topic. If you tell me you prefer not to talk about it, I'll drop it right now."

I asked Bubby for half an hour to think it over. She agreed and left me to my thoughts.

* * *

I did have social problems. It hadn't always been that way. In the lower grades, I was friends with everyone. At that age, who even knew about being "accepted" or "rejected"? It had begun in the last couple of years. Ever since then, I'd been in trouble.

A few powerful girls rule over our class. In the beginning, I was their friend, but one day they decided to exclude me because of an argument I had with one of them. They made sure that everyone knew it wasn't a good idea to be my friend. Suddenly, I was like some kind of an outcast.

And that's the way it's been ever since. I kept trying to be friends with them, but they put me down and rejected me.

I felt like this is how it was going to be for the rest of my life, and there was nothing I could do about it.

I never told my parents what was going on. I'm not sure why. Maybe I felt ashamed, like it was somehow my fault that I was a social outcast. But how was

I to blame? I couldn't figure it out. Now that I thought about it, it seemed like a great idea to talk to Bubby about it.

When Bubby came back, I said, "I want to talk to you about it." I burst out crying and choked out through my tears, "No one wants to be my friend. And it's going to be that way forever!"

Bubby hugged me.

After I had calmed down, Bubby said to me, "I don't have any magical way of instantly fixing things, but I do think I can help you with this. It won't be easy. You'll have to do things that will be hard for you. But if you're willing to do them, you'll see a change in the very first month. It will get easier as you go along. It will be hard at first, but then it will get very easy."

It sounded like a plan. I waited to hear the details.

But Bubby was in no hurry. "Before we begin, I want to ask you a few questions. You can answer only the ones you feel like answering."

Bubby asked me dozens of questions. She asked the names of the most popular girls in the class, the relationships between them, the different groups, the type of girl each of my classmates was, which of them hurt me or others, which one was more easygoing, who gave me the cold shoulder, and who spoke to me occasionally. Bubby told me not worry that I'd saying *lashon hara* because it was *l'to'eles* and allowed.

Bubby's questions asked helped me see for myself what was going on in my class. She asked about things I'd never thought about. Now that I did think about them, I had a clearer picture.

As I was talking, Bubby took notes. Then she took a few minutes to study those notes and draw a diagram. When she finished, she turned the paper around to show me what she had drawn.

It was a chart of the relationships between girls in our class. Each girl's name was connected (or not) to another girl (or more) by an arrow. I saw two groups of four girls connected to each other, and another group of six. I looked for my name. I found it next to eleven girls who, like me, weren't part of any group.

"Notice what's going on here," Bubby said. "There are three groups, as you can see. You keep trying to join two of the groups but without any success. You feel there's no way for you to belong to either of them. You're right—and wrong. You're right that there's no way to break into either of these groups. But there is a way to make these groups want to include you."

"What do I need to do to get in?" I asked.

"You have to stop wanting to," Bubby said.

* * *

What a strange answer. But it made me curious about how it could work.

Bubby quoted *Pirkei Avos* where it says, "Honor runs away from the person chasing after it." She said that social connections work the same way. "Whoever runs after the group will find the group running away from him. What you've been doing until now, Tzippy, is running after girls who aren't even worth it. Their power stems from the fact that you and the other girls run after them. The minute you stop doing that, two things will happen. One is that they'll stop getting a free gift they don't deserve. Two, and most important of all, is that you'll stop making your success dependent on belonging to their group. It will depend solely on you and your actions."

Bubby then presented me with the plan, which she called a "social diet."

"You know what a diet is in terms of food," she said. "A person who doesn't eat right gains or loses too much weight. It's the same for social connections. So you're going to go on a diet. You'll stay away from society in order to come back to it in a different way, with self-confidence that doesn't depend on anyone else, just you."

* * *

I followed the "diet plan" for the next three months. It wasn't easy, just like a food diet isn't easy. You see a yummy chocolate cake, but you hold yourself back from even a taste. You see a few friends, and you want to talk to them, but you hold yourself back because you know that if you flatter them or run after them, they'll look down on you, and you'll feel smaller than you do already.

It was hard, but the more I weaned myself from the need to be part of their group and the less I ran after them, the better I felt about myself. I managed just fine without those snobby cliques I'd kept trying so hard to push my way into.

Something else happened, too. Remember the other eleven girls who weren't part of any group? Well, I became friends with them. Slowly but surely, with my bubby's encouragement and guidance, we became the biggest group in the class. Not a snobby clique that excluded others, but a group that felt good about itself.

Now I didn't feel lonely. I wasn't an outsider anymore. I didn't feel a need to push my way into a group of girls who didn't want to be friends with me (or who maybe did but were afraid to because of peer pressure).

Within three months, our class was a different class. The group I'd brought together became "the class," and the snobs felt left out. Suddenly they were the ones asking if they could join us in some activity we planned or be part of our conversation.

We didn't reject them, so there was no conflict. Girls respected us for that.

My social standing went from zero to a hundred. All the problems vanished as if they'd never existed.

At the end of the year, when I was so happy, Bubby said to me, "You realize, though, that you forgot something important."

"What?"

"I owe you an afikoman present, but you haven't even mentioned it," she teased.

How could I have forgotten?! A trip to Europe with Bubby and Zeidy!

"You know, Bubby, you promised me a great gift, and I'm not going to give it up, but you should just know that I've already gotten my afikoman present."

"What do you mean?"

"If there was a special wish that I didn't even ask because I never dreamed it could come true, it was that

BEN GURION AIRPORT
דבורה
בנדיק

my social situation would improve. And now, thanks to you, not only did it improve, I feel like every minute of being in class is fun. That's the best afikoman present I could wish for."

"So, you're giving up the trip?"

"Never!" I gave her a big hug. "I heard that after a strict diet I'm allowed to treat myself."

Tefillin of Shalom

My name is Shalom.

I'm thirteen and a half, and I live in Netivot.

I'm named after my great-grandfather, who died several decades ago. His name was Shalom, which means "peace," and he was just like his name: a man of peace. He was someone who respected others and would rather give in than argue.

I grew up hearing stories about him. People still talk about his outstanding *middos* and what a special person he was.

One story in particular stands out, and that's the one I want to tell you. I heard it for the first time just before my bar mitzvah. (I'm warning you, though—one part of this story is very annoying. But I think you'll agree that it's also the most important part.)

The way I heard this story about Zeidy Shalom is a story of its own.

When I turned twelve, my parents began looking for a hall for my bar mitzvah. They finally found one they liked and booked it. They sat with the owner and worked out all the details, down to the menu, the color scheme, the band—everything.

A month before my bar mitzvah, when we went to finalize with the hall, the hall's manager told us that he'd already finalized with a different family.

My parents were shocked. "How could you give the hall to someone else after we booked it?"

"You didn't give me a deposit," he said, "so I don't owe you a thing."

"But you didn't ask us for one," my parents said.

"True," he said, "but then these people came. They pressured me to let them have the hall and gave me a check. You know what they say, 'A bird in the hand is worth two in the bush.'"

He inadvertently let slip the name of the people who had taken the hall. It was a family that davened in our shul.

We stood there dumbfounded.

"Why?" I cried in frustration, more to myself than anyone else.

My mother nearly fainted. "We can't keep quiet about this," she said. "We have to tell them. If necessary, we'll go to the *rav* about it."

My father was quiet, and then he said, "Let's calm down. We can fight this, but we can also look for a different hall."

I wasn't surprised by my father's reaction. He's just like my grandfather and great-grandfather, a man who flees from conflict like he's running away from a dangerous fire.

I was upset about what the hall manager had done. Why should we give in to people like that who were willing to step all over us? And what about my bar mitzvah? We'd planned everything around this hall. How would we find another hall now, a month before my bar mitzvah?

I started crying. My parents tried to calm me down. My father reassured me that he would find a different hall. Besides, he said, in our family, we don't get involved in arguments.

I didn't feel good about it. They'd taken away my bar mitzvah hall a month before my bar mitzvah. Why should we keep quiet about it? Why should we be the ones to give in?

When we got home, I ran to my room, sat on my

bed, and buried my head in my hands. That's how bad I felt right then.

A while later the door opened. My father came in and sat on my bed.

"Shalom," he said, "I want to tell you a story."

This is what he told me.

* * *

I was twelve and a half (my father said) when my grandfather Zeidy Shalom suddenly passed away. I was very close to him, just like you're close to his son, your Zeidy Weinstein.

After the shivah, Zeidy Shalom's children—my father and his siblings—divided up the inheritance. His apartment went to the youngest brother. The other brothers were all in business, but he learned in kollel full time and needed the money more than they did. Zeidy had made his wishes known years before his passing, so this came as no surprise.

From the money left in savings accounts, the brothers set aside a generous amount to write a *sefer Torah* that would be dedicated in Bubby and Zeidy's memory. They then divided the rest of the assets between themselves. For valuable items, such as Zeidy Shalom's siddur, tefillin, watch, and the candlesticks that belonged to Bubby, who had died several years earlier, they made a lottery.

Before the lottery, my father, your Zeidy Weinstein, said that he hoped he would get his father's watch. It was very old, and it wasn't a brand name or made of gold, but it still worked. He told me he didn't want the watch for its dollars-and-cents value but because "when I wear it, I'll feel that my father is always with me."

I hoped that for his sake he would get the watch.

But my father didn't get the watch. It went to a different brother, Zelig, my uncle, who was older than my father but not the *bechor*.

My father was disappointed, but he felt consoled because he'd gotten his father's tefillin. Before the lottery, his brother Zelig had said he hoped he'd win the tefillin. Now, after the lottery, my father asked his brother if he would like to trade.

"I wanted the tefillin," Zelig told him, "but a lottery is a lottery."

My father didn't say a word, but I heard my mother tell him, "You could have argued with him. After all, he wanted the tefillin to begin with."

"I would never want to cause even the smallest argument over my father's inheritance," my father said.

"I want to give him *nachas*. To my father, peace always came first."

A month before my bar mitzvah, my father told me that he'd thought about it a lot and decided that I should be the one to receive Zeidy Shalom's tefillin, the tefillin he'd won in the lottery, because I had been so close to Zeidy Shalom. He showed me that he'd gotten new straps put on and said he'd had a *sofer* inspect the *parshiyos*.

"The letters look like they were written yesterday," the *sofer* told him.

The tefillin looked brand new, but they were still "Zeidy Shalom's tefillin."

I asked my father why he didn't want to use the tefillin himself. He said he'd given it a lot of thought and decided that this way, Zeidy Shalom's legacy would be passed down to my generation and to those who came after me.

"He's in my heart anyway," my father said, "even without the watch."

I saw how he still wished he'd gotten his father's watch.

I put on tefillin for the first time at the Kosel. My father and I both had tears in our eyes as he helped me wind the straps.

The bar mitzvah day got closer. My parents had ordered a hall and a keyboardist and everything else we needed. I felt sad that my Zeidy Shalom wouldn't be there with me, but at least I had his tefillin.

Ten days before my bar mitzvah, my Aunt Rachel, Uncle Zelig's wife, came to our house.

She seemed nervous. "I didn't come for a visit," she said. "Zelig sent me."

"What's the problem?"

"There's no problem," Rachel said. "Actually, everything's fine. He just sent me."

"Why did he send you?"

"I'm sorry to have to say it, but he had a dream last night in which his father said that he wants Zelig to use his tefillin."

I was in my room with the door open, so I couldn't help but overhear the conversation. I felt the blood drain from my face. I clenched my hands tightly, waiting to hear what my father would say.

"Abba came to him in a dream?" my father asked. I could tell he found it hard to believe.

"Yes," she said. "In a dream. He came and told him that he should wear his tefillin."

"It sounds a bit strange," my father said. "But if our father gave Zelig a message, we must listen to it."

"You know, Rachel," my mother said quietly, "there's a problem, because the tefillin belong to Aryeh now. He began putting them on two weeks ago."

"I know," Rachel said. "I told that to Zelig, but he still sent me to tell you about his dream."

I knew that if it were up to my father, he would have handed over the tefillin after the first sentence. But now there was a serious reason not to; they were mine, so they weren't his to give.

It was a choice between his brother or his son. And I was sure he would choose me.

My father came into my room and sat down next to me.

He spoke fast. "I know you'll find this hard to understand, but I'd like you to let me give your tefillin to Uncle Zelig."

I looked at him but said nothing.

"Is that okay with you?" my father asked me.

I didn't say anything.

"I need your consent, Aryeh," my father said. "I won't give away your tefillin without your consent, and I would very much like you to agree. I'll explain it to you another time."

I looked at him and started to cry.

He hugged me. "If you don't want to, I won't."

I pulled away from him, went over to the drawer where I kept the tefillin and took them out. I handed them to him and then flung myself on my bed and burst out crying.

My father sat there for a while, thinking it over.

Then I heard him leave the room.

"Here," I heard him say to Aunt Rachel. "Please take the tefillin."

"This is so uncomfortable," I heard her say. "Zelig sent me."

"Yes, we understood that," my father said.

Then I heard him ask, "By the way, did you bring the watch?"

"Uh, no. All Zelig said was that he dreamed about his father's tefillin. He didn't dream anything about the watch."

Silence.

"Ah," I heard my father say. "Okay, then. Let the watch remain with him as well."

"You agree to that?" Rachel asked, sounding even more miserable than before.

"Yes," my father said. "He had a dream. What can I say?"

"I just want you to know that I didn't want to come," she said. "Zelig told me to."

תפילין

"It's okay," my father said. "You're a good woman who does as her husband asks her to."

"So it's okay?" she asked.

"It's perfectly fine," my father said. "What can I do? My father appeared in a dream."

"Then goodbye," she said.

* * *

"What?!" I said after my father finished telling me the story. "Do you mean to say that Zeidy Weinstein just took your grandfather's tefillin from you and gave them to his brother?"

"That's exactly what he did," my father said. "I burst into tears and screamed, 'Why? Why?' just like you did at the hall. My father hugged me. I was sobbing. As he held me, I felt him crying too.

"'The day will come when you will thank me for this,' my father told me. 'You'll always remember this. Hashem sent me a very big test, perhaps the hardest test of my life so far. I'll make it up to you, I promise. But I'm telling you that what you just saw will stand you in good stead throughout your whole life. A person never loses out by giving in.'"

I looked at my father. He had tears in his eyes. I saw that though this story had happened decades ago, it was more than just a memory. It was still alive for him.

"Now I'll tell you the rest of the story," my father said. "Thirty years have passed since then. As you know, your Zeidy Weinstein died two years ago. You're lucky that you had the *zechus* to know him. He left this world pure and clean, loved and admired. To this day, people tell me stories about his *middos*, his dedication, his giving, and especially his wisdom.

"Over the years, I came to realize how much is gained from giving in. I've acted that way with friends and family—you children included—with bosses and employees, with neighbors and acquaintances, and with everyone else. Always give in, be humble, and compromise.

"I saw people whose lives were suddenly destroyed because they couldn't be flexible. I saw people who destroyed their families, lost friends, and fought with their neighbors. I watched as people filled their lives with quarrels and strife while I, *baruch Hashem*, live a peaceful, quiet life. I'm at peace with myself and my surroundings because of what I learned from my wonderful father, your Zeidy Weinstein, may he rest in peace: Give in, give in, give in!

"And now," my father said, "I'm going to surprise

you. I'd planned on doing so in two weeks, but because of this incident with the hall, I decided to do it right now. Do you remember that six months ago my Uncle Zelig died? The one who received my tefillin?"

Of course I remembered. I'd never really known Uncle Zelig, though, because he lived in Holon, and he was my father's uncle, not mine.

"You arranged his *levayah*, burial, and shivah, didn't you?" I said.

"Yes. His children didn't know to whom to turn or what the customs were," my father said. "But there's something you don't know. On the last day of the shivah, his widow, Aunt Rachel, asked to have a word with me privately. Yes, the one who came to our house then. She's eighty-seven now."

"'Look, Aryeh,' she said, 'there are two things here that I think you should have. Sad to say, but my children aren't as religious as Zelig and I were. None of them asked me for their father's tefillin, so perhaps you can take them.'

"She handed me the tefillin bag and began to cry.

"'You were a little boy,' she said, 'so you don't know what an angel your father was. I will never forget him.' She used a tissue to dab at her eyes, not understanding why I too was moved to tears. I'd been in my room when she came to ask for the tefillin, so she had no idea that I knew what had happened all those years ago. I guess she'd forgotten that those tefillin had already been given to me and that I was the one who had agreed to give them up.

"The tefillin came back to me for the second time after thirty years," my father said, "and as soon as I got them, I knew I was going to do what Zeidy Shalom would have wanted me to do. I'm going to give them to my son, who will celebrate his bar mitzvah next month.

"I've already had them checked and had the straps and *battim* renewed."

My father picked up a velvet bag I hadn't noticed and handed me my tefillin, the ones I'll use my whole life, *b'ezras Hashem*. Zeidy Shalom's tefillin.

I was in awe. What a story! And now I had those very same tefillin.

A few days later, we found an even better hall than the one the other people had taken from us. Not only did we avoid a fight, but we didn't lose anything—because when you give in, you don't lose out.

My tefillin look the same as everyone else's, but they're special because of the parchments inside. These tefillin have gone through three generations of people in our family who knew how to give in for the sake of peace.

And now I'm the fourth.

The name embroidered on the velvet bag is Shalom, which is my name...and my great-grandfather's. And now you know the story behind it.

These are the tefillin of shalom—triple meaning.

Once Upon a Time...

My name is Yael.

I'm eleven, and I live in the center of the country. I'm a popular girl and also somewhat sensitive.

Okay, not just "somewhat" sensitive. More like super sensitive.

Often I feel hurt by what people say to me. I don't always tell anyone how I feel, but my parents always want to know what I'm thinking, and they usually find out. But when they hear why I feel hurt, they usually say it's a silly reason and that I shouldn't feel hurt by something like that.

Let me give you an example. For instance, if my friends and I were jumping rope and my feelings were hurt because I got out a few times, my parents would tell me that while it's very disappointing to be out in

a game, what is there to feel hurt about? That's how they saw it.

So I explained to them that I felt hurt because everyone saw I was out.

And they explained to me that if someone didn't mean to hurt my feelings, then there's no reason to feel hurt. And even if someone did mean to hurt my feelings, I can still decide not to feel hurt.

I'm glad my parents are trying to make me feel better, but at the same time, I find it a little bit, um, hurtful that they don't agree with me that it was hurtful.

I think you get the point.

* * *

One day I went to visit Bubby. She lives in a different city, so I don't get to see her as much as I'd like to.

As usual, she gave me a generous piece of her special cake and all sorts of sweets and treats. Then she sat down across the table from me and said, "I have a story I want to tell you. It's about a girl just your age, and it took place over sixty years ago. The girl's name was Raizy.

"Raizy went through a period when she was very sad," Bubby said. "She'd wake up feeling sad, get dressed feeling sad, go to school feeling sad, come home feeling sad, do homework feeling sad, and go to sleep feeling sad.

"I must tell you that in those days parents didn't have the same kind of relationship with their children as parents do nowadays. They loved their children, but they didn't express it the same way. Today, at the first sign a child is unhappy, his parents will ask him, 'What's wrong? Why are you sad? How can we help you?' But back then, a child could be sad for a long time before anyone noticed. And when they did, they'd just tell him, 'Don't feel so sorry for yourself. Wipe that sad expression off your face and carry on.'

"From the way it sounds, you might think that parents back then were cruel," Bubby said, "but they weren't. Not at all. They were good parents, and if there were a real problem, they'd help. It's just that they didn't think everything was a problem. And guess what, Yaeli? Who do you think has more inner strength and fortitude, today's children or those of previous generations?

"Today's children, right?" I offered. I wasn't sure though.

"Wrong," Bubby said. "Today's children are so coddled and spoiled that they turn out a lot weaker and more fearful. They find it a lot harder to cope with life."

Bubby had a few more uncomplimentary things to say about today's kids, but I don't want to hurt anyone's feelings by repeating them. I felt hurt hearing them, not just for myself but for all of us kids everywhere.

"And the children of previous generations?" I asked. "Were all of them strong?"

"I don't think any of them were strong."

That took me by surprise.

"They were regular, ordinary children. I think that today's children are spoiled and weak, so by comparison, the children of generations past were stronger."

"Is that the story you wanted to tell me?"

"No, that's not the story, it's only the introduction to the story," Bubby said.

* * *

"As I was saying, many years ago, there lived a girl named Raizy," Bubby began. "She was a smart little girl, and a good one too, but one year during the last two months of school, right before summer vacation, Raizy was sad and upset. She didn't sleep well or do well in school.

"It took Raizy's parents two weeks to realize that Raizy wasn't acting like her usual self. They started paying closer attention to her, but they didn't see anything that would explain why Raizy was so sad and why she found it hard to sleep at night.

"At first they didn't say anything to her, hoping her sadness would go away by itself. But when it didn't, they became worried and sad too, because even back then parents didn't want their children to be sad. They wanted them to be happy, just not spoiled, as I already explained to you.

"One day when Raizy came home from school, her mother sat with her on the couch and said, 'I've noticed that lately you've been coming home from school sad. Can you please tell me why?' Then she added, 'Your father and I wanted to take you on a trip during summer vacation, but since you're so sad, we're not sure we'll be able to. Do you have something to tell me?'"

Bubby paused.

I was pretty sure *my* parents would have promised me a vacation trip if only I'd tell them what was bothering me, but back then, parents would threaten to cancel the trip. It sure didn't sound easy to be a kid back then.

"Raizy was silent," Bubby continued. "She didn't want to tell her mother why she was sad, mostly because her mother was part of the reason.

"Her mother tried again and again, but when she

saw that Raizy wasn't willing to tell her what was bothering her even after she threatened not to take her on a trip and even when she didn't put any chocolate spread on her bread, she decided to ask Raizy's father to speak to Raizy.

"Once upon a time, fathers hardly spoke to their children," Bubby told me. "A father was someone who supported the family, someone you needed to honor and respect…and even fear a little. Children weren't truly afraid of their father because they knew their father loved them and took care of them and protected them. Actually, children back then had fewer fears than today's children because back then their parents told them they had nothing to be afraid of, and they trusted their parents. Children back then looked up to their parents. In their eyes, parents were big, strong adults who always knew what to do. They might have lost out on the feeling that parents are like friends. But on the other hand, their parents were parents—and you had to trust them and do what they said.

"So Raizy's mother said to Raizy's father, 'Maybe you could take Raizy for a short walk to find out why she's sad. I tried asking her, but she won't tell me. Maybe she'll tell you.'

"And then she whispered in his ear, 'If she doesn't

tell you, give her a few *potches* and then she'll tell you.'

"She thought Raizy didn't hear what she whispered," Bubby said, "but Raizy heard every single word."

"What are *potches*?" I asked Bubby.

Bubby laughed and then shook her head. "What kind of a generation is growing up? A generation that doesn't know what *potches* are? A *potch* is a little slap."

I looked at her wide-eyed. What did she mean?

"You know, a slap. What's not to understand?"

I burst out laughing. I don't know what was so funny. Was it the word *potches*? Or was it the thought of giving a child *potches* so he'd say why he was sad. It was like a joke I'd never heard before. I didn't know whether to be afraid of life as it was back then or to long for it.

"Anyway," Bubby continued, "Raizy's father agreed and even told her mother, 'You know I enjoy going for walks with Raizy.'

"That came as a big surprise to Raizy because her father had never told her, not even one single time, what he liked and what he didn't like, so she certainly couldn't know that he liked to take a walk with her.

"'So tomorrow,' Raizy's mother said, 'surprise her and pick her up after school. Take her to buy a licorice and go for a walk.'"

I had no idea what a licorice was, but I didn't ask Bubby because I didn't want to interrupt the story and also because I figured it must be candy from back then. I don't think I would like a candy called "a licorice."

"The next day," Bubby continued, "when Raizy finished school she saw her father waiting for her at the front gate.

"After he bought a licorice for her and one for himself, and they were walking down the street, he said, 'Why have you been looking so sad lately? Maybe you have something to tell me?'

"Raizy was silent.

"Her father pleaded with her. 'Raizy, it's not good that you're not talking to your parents. Maybe you're in trouble, but if you don't talk, you'll be in trouble all the time. I went through tough times when I was a little boy, and I was also sad and worried. I also didn't talk to my parents or my teacher. But even if I had wanted to tell, no one asked. And here we are asking you, Raizy, what's bothering you. If you tell us, we can help you get out of trouble.'

"'Will you give me a *potch* if I don't tell?' Raizy asked her father.

"Her father laughed. 'Your mother said that purposely for you to hear, but you're a smart girl. No, I'm not about to give you even a single *potch*, because not talking will hurt you more. Come on, tell me and see what happens.'

"Raizy was silent a little longer. A moment before her father finished his licorice, she said, "I don't think Ima loves me.'

"'Why would you think such a thing?!' her father exclaimed. 'Of course Ima loves you! She loves you very much.'

Raizy burst into tears, and then she told her father everything.

"'One night after I went to sleep,' Raizy said, 'I heard you and Ima talking, and Ima said, "I don't know what to do with Raizy. I just can't seem to get along with her. I can't stand being in her presence. I'm sick and tired of her. I can't take it anymore. I have no more patience for her. I did once, but my patience has ended. I think I'll just leave, and that'll be that."

"'That's what I heard, Abba. I heard everything. That's when I found out that Ima doesn't love me,' Raizy said. She looked up at her father. She didn't know what he would say. Would he be angry that she had overheard a private conversation between him and her mother?

"To her surprise, her father started laughing.

"Raizy had never seen her father laugh so hard. He held his sides and laughed and laughed until he nearly fell to the sidewalk laughing.

"Raizy didn't understand what was so funny about her mother not loving her and not having any patience for her and wanting to leave her. She just didn't understand.

"After her father stopped laughing, he said, 'Raizy, darling, your mother works at a pharmacy, doesn't she?'

"'Yes, but what does that have to do with it?'

"'Do you remember the name of the head pharmacist?'

"Suddenly Raizy understood. 'Her name is Raizy!'

"'Now do you understand? Your mother wants to leave the job because her boss Raizy irritates her and bosses her around and she can't take it anymore. Ima meant someone else, but you thought she meant you.'

"Raizy's father laughed again. This time Raizy joined in, and her laughter was one of relief and joy.

"After a whole month of sadness, Raizy realized that her mother didn't hate her and didn't want to leave her and that everything she'd been thinking was one big mistake.

"When they finally stopped laughing, Raizy's

father said to her, 'It's a good thing that you finally decided to talk. Next time when your mother asks you to tell her what's bothering you, tell her. Maybe even go to her before she asks you. You could have said, "Ima, why don't you like me?" If you had done that, you wouldn't have been sad for no reason. Not even for a second.'"

* * *

"That's the story," Bubby said. "Did you like it?"

"Of course I liked it," I said. "It's one of the best stories I've ever heard."

"Really?"

"Really," I replied. "The girl in the story was you, wasn't she?"

"That's right," Bubby said. "Today everyone calls me Shoshana, which means 'rose,' just like Raizy means 'rose' in Yiddish, and this story happened to me."

We sat there in silence. I pictured my Bubby as a young girl named Raizy, feeling hurt.

"Do you have any idea why I told you that story?" Bubby asked me.

It only took me a few seconds to know the answer.

"Yes, Bubby, I think I do. Before I feel hurt, I should first find out whether there's a reason to feel hurt.

Don't worry, Bubby. I won't make the same mistake you did."

As soon as I said that, I regretted it. Maybe I'd hurt her feelings.

"Bubby, did I hurt your feelings? Are you upset by what I said?" I asked her.

Bubby laughed. "What do you think? Isn't it a perfect example of what I was telling you? Don't feel hurt when there's no reason to."

In Search of Justice

My name is Uri.

I'm thirteen, and I'm in the eighth grade.

I'm the friendly type who gets along with everyone. There's one other thing you should know about me: I like things to be fair. It's very important to me that everything goes according to the rules and is done honestly. I can't stand it when someone is treated unfairly.

If there's any kind of argument in our class, I'll always take the side of the one who's right—even if he's a weaker kid and it doesn't pay socially to take his side.

Over the years I've learned that lots of kids tend to side with the majority or with the more powerful kids. They don't always check the facts but just take sides based on what's good for them personally.

I've never been able to understand it. I talked it over with my father, of course without using anyone's name or saying any revealing details. I asked him why I was the only one who saw things the way I did and why the others weren't interested in seeing justice done.

"It's not only children who are like that, Uri," my father said, smiling. "Plenty of adults won't always fight for the person who has truth and right on his side.

"You've got to understand," he explained. "It's not that they're against justice. It's just that they take themselves into consideration too. And if justice is found in a place where it doesn't pay for them, well, they prefer not to get involved. They'll say, 'Why look for trouble?'"

That bothered me a lot. "Why would an adult stand by and watch an injustice taking place?" I wondered. "What kind of person doesn't care about seeing justice done?"

"Suppose someone with a gun threatened your friend," my father said to me. "Would you run to stand between your friend and the gun? Would you take a bullet for him?"

That was too big a question for me. I didn't know what to answer.

My father answered for me. "You wouldn't do it, Uri," he said. "You wouldn't do it because it's forbidden according to halachah. *Chayechah kodmim*—your life is no less precious than your friend's, and your job is to first protect your own life. It's very important to save a life, but Hashem commands us to first be responsible for ensuring our own safety."

I thought about that and then had a question. "But Abba, you told me about an Israeli officer named Roi Klein who threw himself on a grenade to save his fellow soldiers."

"Roi Klein," my father said, "saw that he and the five men in the unit he commanded were all about to be killed in an ambush. He decided to take action to at least save the other five, even if he was killed in the process. That's why he's considered a hero, because he sacrificed himself to prevent harm to others. That kind of courage is rare."

My father recalled another story about a man who bravely jumped into the water to save a drowning child and died in the attempt.

"He didn't think he would die," my father said. "He made a heroic attempt to save the child's life because it wasn't certain that he would lose his own life by doing so."

My father and I talked about bravery and courageous acts to help others, but I was still left with one big question. How was it possible for people to hear about injustice and not do everything in their power to stand up for the truth? Even worse, how could some people remain friends with the ones committing the injustice just because they were afraid of them or because it was worth their while?

I made my decision. I would never be like that. I'd fight for justice no matter what.

I soon got a reputation for being a stickler for fairness and doing what's right. Kids got used to the fact that I wouldn't bend the rules even if it would be to my advantage. And you know what? They respected me for it. I didn't encounter a single situation where I suffered socially because I stood up for someone.

* * *

Now for my story.

There's a block of stores in my neighborhood that everyone calls "the shopping center." It's a stretch to call them that because not a single store stayed in business for more than a few months. Every so often someone would take over a store and open an ice cream parlor or a falafel place or a kids' clothing store. But they'd shut down after only a few months in business, and then another store would open until it too failed.

The place got rundown—broken windows, no lighting. It was an eyesore. But people still came to rent stores, and every time they did, we all knew it wouldn't be long before they, like the others before them, would lose money and eventually close up shop.

Of course, no one told the newcomer this was going to happen because we all hoped that this time the new store would make it.

When I got older, I realized that all the stores belonged to one person. He was renting them out but not doing too well at it. He had a neglected store that sold random stuff like toys that had been sitting there so long they were covered with dust, and household items that no one bought.

I always felt bad for him. There he was, sitting inside his store or standing at the front door, with not a customer in sight.

* * *

One day, workmen came to the row of stores and started renovating three of them.

They even went so far as to break down the wall between them to make one big store.

My friends and I stopped by almost every day to watch them work. First, they tore things apart, and then they brought in construction crews to rebuild and renovate.

Finally, the new store took shape. After they painted, they brought in state-of-the-art display cases and the latest in lighting. In just a few months, the huge store seemed about ready to open its doors. We wondered what it would sell.

One day as we were watching, a big truck drove up, and workmen unloaded commercial refrigerators and freezers. Another truck brought shelving. Now we knew what kind of a store it was: a brand-new supermarket for our neighborhood.

The whole neighborhood turned out for the opening. Everyone came to see the new store, to look around and admire the displays, and also to buy the products that suddenly looked of much better quality and more exclusive than what we were used to—maybe because they were.

As we left we passed the man in the old store. He looked even sadder and more miserable than ever. The contrast between his pathetic little store and the sparkling new store that had just opened was striking.

I told my father about it, and he said, "Well, at least

he's getting rent from that big new store. It should give him a good income."

I was happy to hear that. It made me feel a lot better.

And so, two years went by. We got just as used to the big new store as we were to the dusty old one that no one went near.

* * *

One day, we heard that there was some kind of disagreement between the two store owners.

We kids didn't know what it was about, but according to what we understood, things had reached a point where they'd gone to *beis din*.

One day, a few police cars drove into our neighborhood.

We all ran to see what was going on. They surrounded the shopping center and then a truck arrived. Workers piled out and went into the dusty little store. They soon came out carrying things and before our eyes emptied out the store.

We had no idea what was going on.

As we stood there, the store owner started shouting at the workers to leave his store alone, but the policemen prevented him from interfering with the workers emptying out the store.

כרכול חסד
POLICE
SaLe
SaLe

What a sad sight! If the police hadn't been there, I would have tried to stop the workers from taking the owner's possessions. I couldn't understand why they were doing this to him.

It took them three hours to finish. After they took everything out, they padlocked the store. Now the store owner couldn't get in. They also plastered a big sign on it that said, "This store is closed by police order."

I came home very upset by what I'd seen. I didn't understand why they were treating him like that and why they took his store away from him.

* * *

The next day, the neighborhood learned what had happened. It turned out that the owner of the giant supermarket was the one behind it. Everyone said so. The owner of the small store went and yelled at him.

"You should be ashamed of yourself! You ruined my life!"

People said that not only had the supermarket owner stopped paying rent, he'd forced the poor owner out of his small shop.

That made me mad. What kind of a person would be that mean? He gave you three of his stores to make a big supermarket, and you're making tons of money—so why did you stop paying him rent? What was it to you that he kept selling stuff in his rundown little store?

The evil was just beyond belief.

And I, the warrior for justice, decided to do something about it.

I organized a demonstration in front of the supermarket.

Right after school, my friends and I went to the supermarket. We banged on the front window and shouted, "*Rasha*! Why are you harming another person?"

I told everyone walking into the supermarket, "Don't buy from someone like this. Did you see what he did to the poor man who did him a favor and rented his stores to him? He stopped paying rent to him and also made sure to get him evicted from his little store. Should he be allowed to kill and also inherit?!"

The next day, I made a few improvements. I bought some poster board and wrote slogans on it. Then I got all the kids to go demonstrate against the injustice.

We went over to the store owner, who was sitting outside his locked store, and told him, "We're with you. We won't let this evil man take away your property and drive you away. No way will this happen."

* * *

כול חסד
קונים!
למה
תכה רע

On the third day, in the middle of a loud demonstration that was actually stopping people from shopping at the supermarket, I suddenly felt a heavy hand on my shoulder. I turned around to see who it was.

It was my father.

What was he doing there at my demonstration? For a split second, I thought he'd come to join us. But from the look on his face, I realized that the opposite was true.

"You're coming home with me now," he said. His expression was pleasant as always. You couldn't see anything. But I know him, and I knew he was angry. I knew he didn't want to embarrass me by showing his anger with everyone looking, but I knew it was there. He was mad.

I walked alongside him. He didn't say a thing the whole way home.

When we got home, he told me to go into the living room. I figured he was going to talk to me.

Was I in for a surprise.

Sitting there in the recliner was none other than... the supermarket owner!

My first impulse was to turn around and run. But then I realized my father wouldn't be bringing me to see someone who was going to do something bad to me, so I remained glued to the spot. I stood there trembling, feeling embarrassed.

"Please sit down," the supermarket owner said. "My name Yoel Levy, and I understand that your name is Uri. Nice to meet you."

I didn't say anything.

"I heard from your father that you're a champion of justice. I saw how you organized the demonstrations against me, and I said to myself, any father would want a son like that, who's so sensitive to an injustice that he's not willing to let it pass."

Now I was confused. Why was he calling me a champion of justice when he was the one I was fighting against?

Still I said nothing.

"I want to tell you a few things," he said, "and then you can decide if you want to keep up the demonstrations against me or not."

I sat down on the couch, ready to listen to what he had to say.

* * *

He told me where he lived, that before the supermarket he had worked at various jobs and that he had six children, including twins with special needs.

I know what that means. One special-needs child is a lot of work. Two must be a huge job. But as much as I admired him for raising two special-needs kids, that didn't give him the right to harm the other man and take away his store.

"I'd always dreamed of owning a supermarket. Over the years, I scrimped and saved to make that dream come true. It took twenty years. Once I had the funds, I looked around for the right place.

"One day I got a call from someone, the same man you've been fighting for. He told me that he'd heard I was interested in renting property and said he thought he had just what I was looking for.

"I came to take a look. I was put off when I saw the place. Unoccupied, neglected stores—the whole place had a run-down look to it. I asked around and was told to stay away. 'Every store that's been here lost money and was forced to close.'

"But the man was very convincing. He suggested that I fix up three stores, combine them into one, and that in exchange, he'd lower the rent to make the deal worthwhile.

"I warmed to the idea. The area had potential. I signed a contract with him that stated I would renovate the three stores at my own expense in exchange for his agreement to give me a five-year lease at a bargain price.

"I poured all the money I'd saved into the renovations. As you saw, I turned those stores that no one wanted into one big beautiful store. The supermarket became a popular place to shop, and not only for the residents of this neighborhood. People came from all over. It started making money from the very first day.

"Then, after two years, the owner sent me a letter informing me that I must vacate the store because he was renting it to someone else.

"I said to him, 'But we signed a lease for five years.'

"'True,' he said, 'but there's a clause that says any disagreement between us will be decided by arbitration.'

"I hadn't noticed that clause because the man had seemed to be a very simple person, so I didn't suspect a thing.

"I went with him to this arbitrator, and he listened to what each of us had to say. The whole thing took about ten minutes. And then he said to me, 'You must vacate the premises within a month.'

"I thought I was going to have a heart attack. 'Why?' I shouted. 'Why should I have to leave now after I poured my life savings into the place and haven't made back even half of that?'

"He didn't bother answering me. He just told me, 'If you don't get out, we'll bring in the law, and they'll take you out.'

"I didn't know what to do. I went with my wife to the man—yes, the one you fought so hard to help—and we begged and pleaded with him to let us stay. But nothing moved him, not our pleas or our tears. He acted cruelly toward us, saying, 'That's your problem. You were the ones who spent your money on the place. There's a contract that states that when there's a disagreement we go to an arbitrator. We went to one, and he decided.'

"I made some inquiries and found out that this arbitrator was his partner and not an honest man. But the moment he decided, I had to do what he said.

"I went to a highly respected *rav* who referred me to an expert in such things. 'Go to him,' the *rav* said, 'and tell him to check the property rights.'

"I went to him. Two days later, after checking things out, he got back to me. 'Guess what? The property doesn't belong to that man. It's owned by someone who lives in another country, an Arab country, and he can't get out. For the past twenty-five years, this man has been squatting on land that doesn't belong to him. He built stores on land that's not even his.'

"I couldn't believe my ears.

"I went back to the landlord and told him that I had received information that he didn't own the property but that it belonged to someone else. I even brought him proof. Do you know what he said? He said, 'So? What do you think you can do about it? I want you out.'

"I have a friend who speaks Arabic. He spoke with a big businessman with extensive contacts in Arab countries, and one managed to get in touch with the property owner.

"It turned out that the real owner knew about the man who'd taken over his property and built on it, but he couldn't do a thing about it. Now he wrote asking that this man be removed from the property and the land returned to him, the rightful owner.

"My friend contacted whoever he contacted and managed to write up a contract between the real owner, who was in enemy territory, and me. I began paying the same rent I'd paid the crook to a law firm that saved the money for the man in enemy territory. When he returns to Israel, he'll have money to live on.

"The law office went further. They asked the thief who had taken over the property to leave. Naturally, he refused. That's why the police arrived and forcibly removed him from the store that was never actually his. They even offered me the option of expanding my store to include his, but I didn't want to. As angry as I was at him, I just couldn't do it.

"Now, what do you think about the story?"

I didn't know what to say.

My father handed me some documents, and I glanced through them. It took me less than five minutes to see that the person I'd thought was a victim was actually a thief, while the person I'd thought was a villain was actually a kindhearted man just trying to earn an honest living. He'd almost lost everything because of a heartless man who couldn't have cared less.

My head was spinning.

"I don't know what to say," I said. "I'm so, so sorry."

"It's okay," my father told me. "I told him that you're always on the side of justice. This story gave you a rare opportunity to learn a basic truth. Before you take up the battle for truth and justice, find out where justice lies, because people committing an injustice can masquerade as victims, seemingly virtuous and helpless. Most people aren't like that, but people who are used to lying get very good at it and know how to fool others into believing them."

I was still shocked. My whole body trembled. I couldn't believe what I had done to such an honest person with two special-needs kids who just wanted to realize his dream. And to think that my friends and I had almost ruined his chances of success.

"Don't worry," the man said to me. "I think you learned an important lesson, one that all those who pursue justice need to learn. You learned that you have to check carefully to make sure you're on the side of justice and not injustice. Do you understand the difference?"

I sure did.

We said our goodbyes, and I apologized again and promised to fix what I had damaged.

* * *

The next day I gathered all my friends and told them what I'd been told. I made sure not to say any *lashon hara* but only what was necessary, as my father had instructed me. And then we headed for the supermarket.

I gave each kid a rose (which my father had bought), and we stood at the supermarket entrance and handed them out to shoppers. To each, we said, "This is a great place to shop! The owner is a good man and as honest as they come."

Out of the corner of my eye, I saw the man I'd sided

with just one day earlier. Our eyes met, and I saw that he knew that I knew the truth. He turned and left and didn't come back.

Because I was so enthusiastic about trying to help him when I thought I was fighting for justice, he was sure he'd fooled me. But when he saw I'd found out the truth and knew where justice truly lay, he gave up fighting a man who only wanted to earn an honest living to support his family.

* * *

Here's my takeaway message to kids everywhere: It's good to pursue justice. Don't be tempted to blindly follow the majority or those with power. Go for justice.

But before you fight for it, check very carefully to make sure you're fighting *for* justice and not *against* it.

The Teacher Who Believed in Me

My name is Yossi.

The story I want to tell you concerns every child but not only children... It also relates to our teachers and educators, and soon you'll understand why.

* * *

I'm the fourth child in our family, followed by three more boys. When I was ten years old, HaKadosh Baruch Hu decided that my father should leave us, and when I say "leave," I mean leave without returning.

This changed everything for our family. Aside from the fact that everyone was sad, my mother didn't have money to support us. She didn't have too much patience for us, either. She loves us very much, my mother, but she can't help us.

My mother is what's called an *"olah chadashah"* in Hebrew. That means a new immigrant. She has a strong accent, and I know that sometimes kids make fun of her behind my back. It's like a knife in my heart.

In cheder, I wasn't one of the "top boys," to put it mildly. The truth? Most of the teachers sent me out of the room on a fairly regular basis. Not because they hated me, *chas v'chalilah* (even though sometimes I felt like they did), but because I was a little wild.

Do you know what I'm talking about? I'm not sure I can explain it, but things just seemed to happen around me too fast. Somehow, before I knew what was happening, I'd find myself outside the classroom with a major punishment. In the best-case scenario, it was a writing assignment (though I still can't figure out who would want to read Chapter One of *Pirkei Avos* written in my horrible handwriting). In the worst-case scenario, it meant a bus ride straight home to face my mother's stern expression.

Sometimes I tried to justify myself, to explain to everyone that it wasn't my fault, that it happened even before I thought of it, that the ball was in my hand and I just had to throw it, and what could I do if the rebbi's mug of coffee was sitting there on the corner of the desk?

I know it sounds a little funny, like I'm trying to get out of taking responsibility, but you should know that a lot of kids feel this way. They're frustrated by their own behavior and don't understand why everyone's always mad at them. I'm positive some of the kids reading this know exactly what I'm talking about.

Anyway, the story I want to tell happened when I was in fifth grade.

One day, Ima woke me up with a smile and showed me a gift-wrapped package that was sitting next to my bed. It was a week after school began.

"What is?" I asked her.

"Open it, and you'll see." She smiled as if she had a secret.

I tore off the wrapping paper and nearly jumped for joy. Inside was a package containing four gyroscopes, each a different color, along with a few launchers, one of them a power launcher. It was a really sophisticated set, the kind you don't see every day. It probably cost a lot.

"Wow, Ima! Whose is it?" I asked. "Do you think he'll let me play with it before he takes it?"

"Yossi, this is yours," my mother said. "My brother sent me a few gifts from Russia to give you children. You can play with it as much as you want."

I felt as if a thousand stars burst out shining right there in my bedroom. It was mine!

I took the whole package with me to cheder to show my friends the expensive gift I'd received.

I went into the classroom and put the package on the table where everyone could see it. You probably think I'm one of those kids who likes to brag about all the stuff he has but believe me, I had never had anything. This was the first and only time I'd gotten a brand-new toy that was worth something. I was so happy that I wanted my friends to see how happy I was.

Some of the boys had already arrived, but I was one of the first. I arranged all the parts in the box and then looked at the clock and saw that Shacharis was about to begin, so I decided to wait until recess.

I plowed through my backpack for a few minutes looking for my siddur until I saw it on a table in the back of the classroom. I went over to get it and then turned around to go back to my seat. That's when I saw something strange.

Motty, one of the most popular boys in class, was holding something in his hand that looked very familiar.

It was my new toy.

"Hey! Give it to me! It's mine!"

I reached out to take it away from him.

"Not so fast," Motty said, pushing my hand away. "It's mine."

I was shocked by Motty's chutzpah. He'd lied straight to my face!

"But it's mine!" I tried to grab the gyroscope again. "I brought it from my house. My mother gave it to me!"

"No way!"

The rest of the class surrounded us, taking sides. Most of the kids were on Motty's side. Like I said, I never had any toys of my own, especially the expensive kind. I always borrowed toys from other kids in class...when they were willing to lend them to me.

What could I do? I felt helpless. I tried to grab the gyroscope from Motty again but the other boys surrounded him like a wall, and I couldn't get through. I watched as Motty played with the gyroscope and launcher to his heart's content.

But it was mine!

Tears of rage filled my eyes. I jumped at Motty in a fury and shoved him hard. The atmosphere grew heated, and if the door hadn't opened at that moment, in another few seconds, we'd have been rolling on the floor, battling it out.

In the doorway stood our teacher, Rabbi Leibnitz.

I didn't know him all that well. It was the beginning of the year. But I assumed that soon he too would start sending me out of class just like all my other teachers had done every year.

Rabbi Leibnitz entered the classroom and frowned.

"What's going on here?" he asked quietly and then ordered, "Motty, Yossi, come over here this minute."

We went over to him, both of us breathing hard.

"Rabbi Leibnitz, it's mine!" I cried out, pointing to the gyroscope and launcher still in Motty's hand.

"That's not true! Yossi's lying!" a few kids shouted. "It's Motty's. Yossi's just trying to take it away from him."

There were shouts from all sides and then, to my surprise, Rabbi Leibnitz took the gyroscope and launcher from Motty.

"Let's discuss this calmly to see what's going on," he said gravely, stroking his beard. "Yossi claims the toy belongs to him, while Motty and his friends claim that the toy is Motty's. Correct?"

I quickly nodded.

"If so, we will make a brief clarification," Rabbi Leibnitz continued calmly. "Motty, where did you get this gyroscope?"

Motty stammered that he had brought it from home.

"Who bought it for you?" Rabbi Leibnitz probed. "When did they buy it for you?"

Then he turned to me and asked me a few questions like that. I answered him in a choked voice.

After a few minutes, Rabbi Leibnitz handed me the gyroscope.

"The gyroscope is yours, Yossi," he said. "It's obvious that you're telling the truth."

Was I happy! I took the gyroscope and launcher and quickly moved away. I was very surprised that the teacher had sided with me. It gave me a good feeling. In fact, I felt so good about it that I made a face at Motty.

"Yossi, come back here immediately," I heard Rabbi Leibnitz say sternly.

"What? But—what did I do?" I walked over to him.

"Yossi, please write the entire first chapter of *Pirkei Avos* and bring it to me after recess," Rabbi Leibnitz told me said when I stood in front of him. "You need to learn that even if you win, there's a concept called 'the winner's code of honor.' You don't taunt your friend after you were victorious over him. That's not good *middos*. True, I ruled in your favor. But that doesn't mean you can now do whatever you want. You're a smart boy, Yossi. I'm sure you understand what I'm saying."

I was confused. Rabbi Leibnitz believed me,

something that hadn't happened too often in my life. He had actually looked me straight in the eye and believed what I was saying! Yet the strong rebuke he'd just given me made me feel like I'd somehow failed.

That day I went home with plenty to think about. I decided that I wanted to earn Rabbi Leibnitz's faith in me and prove to him that I could control my actions.

Rabbi Leibnitz told me I should apologize to Motty, and I did. After that, an amazing new time in my life began. Until then, I hadn't made much of an effort to get good grades or not to disturb in class. But now I worked hard to change all that.

Rabbi Leibnitz turned out to be a man who had a heart of gold. He tried to encourage me in every way possible. He told me that he believed in me and in my abilities and said that if I wanted to, I would be able to improve and not repeat the mistakes of the past.

Progress was slow but steady. Before I knew it, I was one of the best students in the class, one of those who always raises his hand to answer the teacher's question, the boy everyone wants to study with for the weekly exam.

* * *

Time passed, and we reached the end of the year.

One day I was learning together with Motty. By now, we were used to being *chavrusas*. The fights we'd had were past history, and now we were good friends.

"...and that's how Rabbi Leibnitz explained it!" I said enthusiastically. "We got it!"

"Right! It's amazing," Motty agreed with a smile. "But the most amazing thing of all is that Rabbi Leibnitz saw who you were right from the first."

"What do you mean?"

"You know. Uh, that story with the gyroscope," Motty said hesitantly. "When he asked me to pretend to argue with you?"

"What are you talking about?"

"Hold it—you don't know about that?" Motty's face turned white as chalk. "Uh, so forget it."

Suddenly I understood everything.

"Rabbi Leibnitz told you to do all that?" I asked with disbelief. "He told you to take the gyroscope from me so that a fake argument would start?"

"Uh, yes," Motty muttered. "I'm so sorry it slipped out."

"Not at all, Motty," I said with a grin. "I'm actually glad you told me. Do you know why Rabbi Leibnitz did it? Because he wanted to restore my faith in teachers—and in myself and my ability to succeed! He wanted to

show me that he believed in me so that I'd see he cared about me. That's the only thing that pulled me up out of the situation I was in!"

* * *

That's the story, about the teacher who believed in me. I discovered that a teacher can help a student rise to the top if only he believes in the student and gives him the feeling that he can do it. As for us kids, all we need to do is believe in ourselves.

Dangerous Weapon

My name is Avi.

I live in Yerushalayim, but that's not where this story takes place. We'll get to that soon.

I'm a naturally curious kid. I'm interested in everything, and I love excitement.

After I read the latest *Kids Speak,* I realized that I also have a story to tell, and I decided to send it in.

It happened on 11 Tishrei 5778/October 1, 2017, the day after Yom Kippur. It was the beginning of Succos vacation, and my father took me with him to build a succah for my grandmother in Elad. After we finished building the succah, I asked my father if I could stay there. I wanted to spend some time with my cousin Michael. My father agreed and went back home to Yerushalayim alone. I stayed with Michael.

Savta asked us to go buy succah decorations, so Michael and I went out to shop. We didn't find anything in the first store, so we continued on to the next. On the way, Michael, who lives in Elad, suggested we go for a walk in the nearby forest.

You'd be surprised, but Elad has a forest right next to it. And it's not that small, either. It's called Kula Forest, and it covers a large area. We walked into the forest and explored.

What I'm about to tell you now sounds like I made it up, but you can check it out easily. It's a hundred percent true. Just ask your parents, and they'll confirm that what I'm telling you now happened just the way I'm telling it.

As we were exploring the forest, we found a few strange metal objects. We recognized a few of them. They were bullets. But there were also some metal boxes. When we opened them, we saw some powder. But the most interesting thing was a round lump of metal with a sort of handle on top. We had no idea what it was. We realized it must be a rare find, maybe even something worth a lot of money.

We had no idea that this "lump of metal" was a hand grenade. In case you don't know what I'm talking about, a grenade is an explosive device that can kill four or five people. The way to set it off is by pulling out the handle. Within five seconds after that, it will explode.

(I know you don't believe me now either, but ask your parents and they'll confirm that I'm not exaggerating by even one word.)

* * *

And then we made a huge, horrific mistake that only mischievous kids like us could do. Instead of leaving all this stuff right where it was and running to tell an adult that we'd found what looked even to us like weapons, we just grabbed the loot and took it with us back to the city. I have no idea why we ignored the possible danger of weapons like that.

What attracted us most was the lump of black metal, and we started playing catch with it.

Today, when I realize what we did, I get scared just thinking about it. We were tossing a bomb back and forth! If it had fallen and the handle had gotten pulled out of place, the grenade would have exploded, and we would surely have been killed, possibly along with a few other people.

All of a sudden, Savta was there.

You're probably thinking the story ends right here

with our savta yelling at us for doing something so foolish.

But that's not what happened. Because even she didn't know it was a hand grenade. Still, she was an adult and realized it was a type of weapon.

When she saw the grenade, she panicked. She grabbed it away and threw it into the nearest garbage bin. She also warned us never to play with things we didn't understand, especially if we didn't know what they were for.

Not for a minute did Savta think she'd made a big mistake right then. Because the minute she turned her back and went into the kitchen, we took the grenade out of the garbage. We had no idea of the danger we were putting ourselves in.

* * *

We went to the front of the building and split up. Michael climbed up onto the slab of concrete over the entryway to the building next to ours, and I stayed on the ground next to the entrance. We continued our game of catch with the grenade, me throwing it up to Michael, and him throwing it down to me.

As we were playing, Michael said, "I wonder what this handle is for."

"Forget it. Just throw to me."

"Just a minute," he said—and pulled the handle. It came off in his hand.

If your parents are reading this story, they're going crazy with stress and anxiety.

What Michael actually did was "pull the pin" out of the hand grenade, which meant it would explode within four seconds.

After he pulled the handle, he threw the lump of black metal back to me. But I missed it, and it fell to the ground at the building's entrance.

3, 2, 1…

BOOM!

The huge explosion terrified the whole neighborhood, and people came running.

Michael was blown off the concrete slab from the force of the blast. I was standing about three feet away from the grenade when it exploded and was blown back around ten feet.

Total silence fell. My ears rang from the explosion. I got up as fast as I could to look for Michael. Meanwhile, Michael was looking for me.

We met, both of us terrified. Blood was pouring from Michael's chest. I pulled off my shirt—not because I was a big expert in emergency care but because we were afraid that Savta would get scared if she saw so much blood—and put it over the wound both to hide it and to stop the blood from gushing out. Later on, we learned that this saved his life.

In shock about what had happened, I grabbed my head in both hands—and I felt a big open wound in my head, which was bleeding heavily. Then I saw that a neighbor's kid was also hurt. Within minutes, Hatzalah and Magen David Adom arrived. There was a big commotion, and everyone was scared.

They immediately evacuated us to hospitals. They took me to Beilinson hospital in Petach Tikvah, and Michael and the other boy to Schneider Children's. After a quick assessment of my condition, they transferred me to Schneider's too. There we were checked thoroughly. I had a piece of metal in my head that had to be removed. I also had some superficial cuts on my back from glass fragments blown out of the building's front door. The third boy had shrapnel (small metal pieces from a bomb) in his leg and stomach, and some other more minor wounds.

But, of the three of us, Michael was the most severely injured. Two pieces of shrapnel had punctured his chest, stopping between his heart and his lungs. The doctors were able to remove one of them easily, but not the other. It was decided not to remove the second piece, which meant that Michael would never be able to exert himself too much.

The recovery process was long and hard and filled with anxiety.

Despite that, everyone recognized that a great miracle had taken place, one that no one could understand. Military personnel who investigated the matter (to find out how explosives and bullets and gunpowder got to the forest near Elad) told me that they hardly knew a case in which someone standing within three feet of an exploding grenade remained alive. They also explained to me how a grenade works. The explosive material inside the grenade explodes the iron into thousands of pieces, each one as deadly as a bullet.

I became a semi-expert on bombs, but I would gladly forgo this knowledge because the other children and I paid for it with our flesh and blood.

* * *

If you don't believe the story (which I admit, sounds totally made up), I invite you to take a look at the headlines of Sunday night, 11 Tishrei 5778/October 1, 2017, the night after the explosion.

The reason I'm telling this story to *Kids Speak* is to

publicly thank Hashem for the incredible miracle He made for Michael and me and the other boy who was there. And also, I need your help to let kids everywhere know not to play with—or even touch—suspicious objects.

Here's the newspaper article with a photo:

3 Children Injured After Playing with Grenade

11-year-old children play with grenade, injure themselves and cause residential building to be evacuated.

Entrance to the building after explosion.

Two children were moderately injured, and another was lightly injured in an explosion that occurred Sunday evening in a residential building on Ben Zakai Street in the central Israeli town of Elad.

The three children, all 11 years old, were treated by Magen David Adom and United Hatzalah paramedics and taken to Beilinson Hospital in Petach Tikvah.

The police's preliminary investigation revealed that the children were playing with an M203 grenade at the entrance of their apartment building, which exploded and caused their injuries. The police are investigating how the children came to be in possession of the grenade.

The explosion caused damage to the building's gas line, authorities said. As a result, all residents were evacuated from the building. A gas technician summoned to the site is currently working to repair the damage, after which the residents will be allowed to return to their apartments.

Sivan Mashiach, a volunteer paramedic with United Hatzalah, said: "I provided emergency first-aid to an 11-year-old boy who was moderately to severely wounded, to another child who was moderately injured, and to another child who was lightly to moderately injured. I also treated a woman who suffered from shock due to the nature of the incident."

Here are a few good rules to follow: If it's not yours, don't touch it. If it looks strange, and you've never seen anything like it before, don't touch it. Explosives are sometimes left in abandoned places, and not every kid knows they're explosives. If you see something that looks suspicious, move far away, warn other people, and notify the police as soon as possible.

We have a lot to thank Hashem for every day. We already know that we have to be careful when we cross the street and that we have to stay away from all kinds of problematic people. Now add this one to the list: Stay far away from a suspicious object.

Yudah's Bonfire

My name is Yehudah, but everyone calls me Yudah.

I'm twelve, and I live in Ma'ale Adumim.

You've got to hear my story. Even though it's about Lag BaOmer and it might not be Lag BaOmer for you now, you'll hear about a lot of things that are important to every kid. It's also a moving story and one you won't hear every day.

First, a little background information: For the past five years I've been in charge of making the Lag BaOmer bonfire.

In case you don't know, to be in charge of a bonfire you don't need an office with a phone and fax. All you need to do is to get a few friends to join you and start planning about a month before Lag BaOmer. You need to think about where to make it, who will be in the group, where to get the wood and where to store it, where and when to build the bonfire, how to stack the wood—in other words, it's a project that needs someone to be in charge.

Usually, the bonfire is named after the one in charge, and since that's me, everyone calls it "Yudah's bonfire."

My bonfire is famous in our area, and lots of kids come to watch me light it. Why? Because it's the biggest one around and the most beautifully built. It also has a lot of gimmicks, some of which everyone knows already from previous years and some of which are kept secret until the bonfire is lit.

Another special thing about my bonfire is that even though only a few of us are in charge, we let everyone come to watch it and enjoy it, unlike some other bonfires where the kids in charge don't let anyone get close and make everything a secret, including the location and the participants. Ours is open to the public. Not that everyone can do whatever he wants. There has to be some order in life, but everyone is welcome to participate.

I think that's one of the secrets of my bonfire. But I guess you realize that if I'm telling you it's not really a secret.

How did I get to be in charge? I have no idea. Maybe because I'm the type who likes to get things done, not just Lag BaOmer bonfires. Even in my family, people count on me to arrange things during trips and parties and all kinds of events. Not that I'm trying to brag or anything. I just want to tell you what happened last Lag BaOmer.

* * *

Right after Pesach, me and six of my friends met to plan the fire's size and location and think up ideas for special surprises. We reviewed what had happened the previous year: other kids found our hiding place and took our wood, and the municipality almost put out our fire because they were worried about the power lines above it. We decided to hide the wood in a different location, with each of us responsible for bringing a certain amount. One boy said his uncle had some old shelves he wanted to get rid of; another said he knew a place where someone had thrown away a closet; a third said his father told him he'd help him find wood.

We set out separately to search for a good hiding place, and it wasn't long before we were set up in my best friend, Duddy's, basement. It even had a lock. The only drawback was the steps going down into it. We decided that we'd just throw the boards in through the side window and drag them up when we were ready to build the bonfire. That part would take some effort, but we were ready for it.

But I wasn't at all ready for what happened next.

* * *

One of the boys in the neighborhood, Ayal, was hospitalized.

Let me tell you a little bit about Ayal.

He lives in our neighborhood, but he doesn't go to our school. He's autistic, so he has some problems with communication.

You can tell right away that Ayal isn't like the rest of the kids because he doesn't talk a lot and even when he does, his speech isn't all that clear. Not that he stutters. It's just that it's hard to understand what he's trying to say. He also smiles to himself a lot.

We kids are okay with him. We're careful not to laugh at him or hurt his feelings. We even include him in our games when we can. Even though he doesn't know how to play that well, we try to make it work out that he enjoys playing but doesn't interfere with the game.

Ayal is always part of the group that builds the

bonfire. We help him bring the wood. It takes longer because two kids need to help him carry the wood, but we want him to feel good about collecting wood just like everyone else.

Right after Pesach, Ayal was hospitalized with pneumonia.

You're probably wondering, "What's that got to do with anything?"

Plenty.

I went to visit Ayal in the hospital nearly every day after school, which is when I normally would have been out leading our group in collecting wood.

To understand the rest of the story, you need to know our schedule.

Pesach vacation ends on 23 Nissan. Lag BaOmer is on the 18th of Iyar. That means there's almost a month to collect wood.

It starts off slowly, but in the week and a half before the bonfire, everyone works extra hard to collect as much wood as possible.

So when Ayal was first hospitalized, no one paid that much attention to the fact that I wasn't out there collecting wood. The pace then was slow and easy. But as we got

closer to Lag BaOmer, my friends noticed my absence.

* * *

One day, my friend Gadi came over to me and said, "Yudah, where've you been? The whole thing is going nowhere without you."

The "whole thing" is the bonfire, in case you didn't get it.

"Look," I said to him, "Ayal is in the hospital, and I have to visit him."

"I know," Gadi said, "but someone has to make a bonfire, don't they?"

"Don't worry about it," I told him. "I think Ayal will be released from the hospital soon, and then I'll put in twice the time and energy. This year's bonfire will be even bigger and better than any year before."

"If you say so," Gadi said.

"If you say so" usually means, "I'm not very happy about it but what can I do?" And that's the way I took it. I didn't dream there was more to it than that.

Over the next few days, there was a strange silence that left me wondering. By the end of the week, it dawned on me that not a single one of my friends was talking about the bonfire.

Too bad I'm neglecting the bonfire, I thought. *I'll talk to the chevrah, and we'll get to work collecting. We'll catch up fast.*

Before that, I went to the basement storage room to see how much wood was already there. I wanted to know how much more we needed to collect.

I looked through the basement window, and my eyes nearly popped out.

The place was empty.

Not a single piece of wood was there. Not even sawdust.

I remembered seeing it filled with boards. That could mean only one thing: someone must have broken in and taken all the wood.

* * *

I ran to the playground and called all the boys in our group. I said I had to talk to them.

They gathered around me reluctantly. "Can't you see we're in the middle of a game?" Yochai grumbled.

"I didn't ask you to come for nothing," I said in a hushed tone, motioning them to come closer. "I was just at the basement. Someone took all the wood!"

I expected to hear cries of shock like, "What?!" "It can't be!" "We've got to do something!"

But my friends looked at each other indifferently, and

then Yochai said, "So? What are you trying to tell us?"

"What am I trying to tell you? That they stole our wood, that's what I'm trying to tell you!"

"Relax. No one stole our wood," Gadi said.

"Don't tell me no one stole it. Were you there? I just came from there. The place is empty. Go see for yourself."

"I know it's empty," Gadi said with barely disguised impatience. "What I meant was that even though the basement is empty, no one stole the wood."

"How could that be? Do you think the boards just walked off by themselves?"

"Something like that," Gadi said, and all the kids laughed.

I didn't like the sound of their laughter.

"Yudah," Gadi said, "*we* took the wood."

"Where to?"

"Timbuktu," Gadi said, and everyone laughed again.

I realized they were laughing at me.

"Wait a sec. You took the wood, and you don't want to tell me where you put it?"

"Something like that," Gadi said. "It's a secret, and besides, I just told you where we took them—Timbuktu."

This time they all roared with laughter.

"You think it's funny?" I said.

"I definitely think it's funny that someone who doesn't lift a finger for the bonfire thinks he's entitled to know where the wood is."

"Hold it," I said. "I'm not someone who 'doesn't lift a finger for the bonfire.' I'm someone who goes to visit Ayal in the hospital. And besides, the bonfire is mine."

"Not anymore," Gadi said. "It's not yours. I think you've already checked out. And they're not going to call it 'Yudah's bonfire' anymore, either. Now it's Gadi's bonfire."

I couldn't believe what I was hearing.

The bonfire had been mine for four years! And Gadi was the one who asked me to make him part of it, which I did. How could he not be ashamed to betray me like that? And why did all my friends suddenly betray me?

"Aren't you guys ashamed of yourselves?" I said to them. "You know exactly why I missed a few days. Bad enough that you're not visiting Ayal, but aren't you ashamed to turn against me for going to visit him?"

"Don't give us a lecture," Gadi said. "If you want to go to the hospital, that's your choice, but someone has to organize the bonfire."

* * *

They all looked at me, waiting for my reaction. Not for a second did I have any doubts about what I was going to do.

"No problem, I said. "There's no question about what I'm going to choose. I'm choosing to do the right thing, to visit Ayal every day, just like I have been. Go ahead and take the bonfire. Or, to be more accurate, go ahead and steal it from me. I hope you feel good about yourselves."

I walked away standing tall and proud as if I couldn't care less.

But the truth was, I did care. A lot. What I'd just found out was so painful. I couldn't believe my friends would double-cross me like that, that they'd take over the bonfire that I'd begun, when I was the one who'd shared it with them! I couldn't believe this was happening to me. It was too much for me to bear.

As I walked away, I felt my shirt getting wet. I looked down and realized it was wet from my own tears that were falling.

I made my way home and shut myself in my room. My mother, sensing that something was wrong, knocked on the door and asked what had happened, but I told her everything was fine, that I was just tired and wanted to rest. Which was true. What I'd just gone

through had drained me, and all I wanted was to do was close my eyes and sleep.

* * *

I woke up an hour later and thought things over again.

I saw that the issue was much bigger than a bonfire being taken away from me. My whole social status was at stake. The boys in the group that used to be mine were no longer my friends. It was as if I had lost all my friends in an instant. And as if that wasn't enough, I knew rumors would soon start flying. When everyone saw they'd taken the bonfire away from me, my social status would drop to zero. Who'd want to be friends with a kid whose friends all left him?

I have to admit that for one small second I wondered, "Maybe I shouldn't have chosen Ayal over my friends?" But that thought was gone even faster than it had come. Maybe my choice of action wouldn't give me an instant reward, but at least I knew I was doing the right thing.

These thoughts didn't come out of nowhere. My parents always taught us to do the right thing no matter what the price. They taught us that the *yetzer hara* always puts a positive spin on what it wants us to do and makes it look like it's to our advantage. To know what we really should do, we have to think not only about "what's in it for me" but about what's the right thing to do.

I knew the right thing to do was to continue visiting Ayal in the hospital. Whatever would be would be.

My only mistake was that I didn't tell any of this to my parents. I thought I could handle it by myself.

Was I wrong.

* * *

Word got around fast. I got the feeling that everyone in class was talking behind my back about me being "kicked out of the bonfire." No longer did I hear them talking about "Yudah's bonfire." Instead, it was "Gadi's bonfire." As if that wasn't enough, my friends—the kids who until only a few days earlier had followed my lead and hung on my every word—had now turned their backs on me and ignored me. That really broke me. I was left all alone.

Hard days followed, days of loneliness. For the first time in my life, I felt what it was like to be without friends, to be on the sidelines. It made me understand what other kids feel when they aren't part of the group, and that made me very sad.

At the same time, I continued to visit Ayal. I'd sit there in the hospital next to his bed. It wasn't much fun. Like I said, Ayal doesn't communicate well, so you can't have a conversation with him like you do with other kids. He's sort of in his own world, but there are openings where you can connect with him.

A week before Lag BaOmer, Ayal was released from the hospital.

Now I was really lonely. Before, at least I had the satisfaction of visiting him. Now I was left without a mitzvah, with a bonfire, and without friends.

As I was sitting home thinking all this, the door-bell rang. I opened the door, and found about a dozen women from the neighborhood standing there.

I had no idea why they'd come. I thought maybe my mother had planned some kind of meeting I didn't know about.

"My mother went out shopping," I told them, "but she'll be back in a few minutes. Do you want me to call her?"

"We didn't come to talk to her," one said. "We came to talk to you."

Huh? What could they possibly want to talk to me about?

I invited them in.

They made themselves at home in the living room.

* * *

Half an hour earlier, Ayal had gone out to collect wood for the bonfire, just like he did every year.

"I want to collect wood for Yudah's bonfire," he told the boys in the playground.

The other boys didn't reply. They didn't know what to say.

Someone said, "There isn't any Yudah's bonfire anymore."

For Ayal, that was no answer. As far as he was concerned, Yudah's bonfire existed, and no one was going to tell him anything different.

Ayal threw a tantrum. He started hitting and kicking the swings. He lay down on the ground and shouted and screamed so loudly that all the mothers in the neighborhood, including his own, came to see what was going on.

"What is it Ayal?" his mother asked him. "What happened? Why are you screaming?"

"I want to collect wood! For Yudah's bonfire!"

"The boys here are collecting wood," a few mothers said. "They'll take you with them."

"To Yudah's bonfire?"

"Yes, of course," they told him.

None of the adults knew what was going on in our world, the kids' world. They didn't know I'd been kicked out of and banished from the bonfire now called "Gadi's bonfire."

"Hey!" Ayal's mother called out to one of the boys. "Are you willing to take Ayal to collect wood with you for Yudah's bonfire?"

"There's no problem taking him," the boy said, "but it's Gadi's bonfire now, not Yudah's."

"Then find me someone who's collecting for Yudah's bonfire," Ayal's mother said.

"There isn't anyone. Yudah isn't making a bonfire."

"What?!" Ayal's mother exclaimed. "Why did Yudah cancel the bonfire?"

"He didn't cancel, he *was* canceled," a few children corrected her, enjoying the unexpected excitement.

"Who canceled it?" the mothers asked.

"His friends. Gadi and the rest. They were mad at him for going to the hospital every day instead of collecting wood, so they took away the boards and stuff and turned it into Gadi's bonfire."

The mothers were in shock.

"I can't believe it," Yochai's mother said. "My son didn't say a word about this to me. I'm so embarrassed."

Lots of the mothers were shocked. One mother said she knew something but "didn't know it was such a big deal."

"Why didn't you think it was a big deal?" the others said to her. "That wonderful boy, Yudah, went to visit Ayal in the hospital every single day, but instead of admiring him the boys pushed him out of his own bonfire. And then they went and stole his wood. What kind of behavior is that? How could our kids do such a thing? Where did we go wrong?"

* * *

The mothers didn't keep quiet about it. They rounded up their kids, letting them know exactly how they felt about what they'd done.

"What did you think you were doing? Go home right now!"

One of the mothers called Gadi's mother, and she came running. When she heard the story, she just started crying, right there in public.

"I won't let it happen," she said. "Where's my son? Where is he?!"

And on the spot, in front of everyone, she told Gadi, "I will not allow this to happen. Not a single one of the mothers will allow this disgraceful thing to take place. Tell me right now what you were all planning."

It was humiliating for Gadi, and he asked his mother if they could move away a little to talk privately, "without everyone listening."

No one could hear what they were saying, but from their expressions, you could see that Gadi's mother was explaining to him that whatever plans he might have had were canceled and that the mothers wouldn't let him take the bonfire away from me.

Gadi and his mother returned to the circle of angry mothers.

"I explained to Gadi," his mother told them, "and he understood, not that it matters. He now realizes his mistake and wants to set things right. He's ashamed to talk to Yudah. I can understand that. He has good reason to be ashamed. I suggest that we all go to Yudah now and ask him to take charge of the bonfire again. He deserves it. And besides, we have to give Ayal 'Yudah's bonfire.'"

And so they came to me.

* * *

I sat there feeling very emotional.

They showered me with praise and gave me so many compliments that it compensated for the difficult time I'd gone through.

A few minutes later, my mother returned home from shopping. She was astonished to see the group in the living room. The mothers told her the story from the beginning (which is how I found out even more details of what had gone on at the playground).

My mother was stunned at first, then sad, and finally, she burst out crying.

She came over to me and said, "Yudah, why didn't you tell me what you were going through? How could such a thing happen?"

"I just couldn't," I told her. "I wanted to, but I just felt that I couldn't."

"How could you keep something so big and painful bottled up inside you?" my mother asked me. "What about all the times I've told you that it's not good to keep everything inside? I feel so bad that you had to go through such a painful experience alone."

If that wasn't embarrassing enough, my mother hugged me and kissed me right in front of everyone. If everything I'd gone through in the past month hadn't been punishment enough, this was the worst punishment of all: my mother kissing me in front of e-v-e-r-y-o-n-e.

I'm just kidding. (But not entirely…)

The mothers told me that their sons were sorry for

what they'd done. They said the bonfire was being returned to me and would be called "Yudah's bonfire" again. All the parents would come when I lit the bonfire to give me support and to signal to their children the kind of behavior they expected of them.

I was touched. My troubles were over. But I also had something I wanted to say.

"I want to thank everyone for caring about me, but during these past few weeks, I realized that I had something to improve too. I think it was a mistake to call it 'Yudah's bonfire.' It's everyone's bonfire. Every kid would like the bonfire to be called by his name, so why was I the only one who had that privilege? When I saw how quickly my friend took over the bonfire, and how quickly all my other friends followed him, it showed me that secretly they all wished they were in my place. They were just too afraid to show it. But the minute they could, they went and did it. It hurt to realize this, but it got me thinking.

"I don't want the bonfire to be called 'Yudah's bonfire.'"

"So what do you want it called?"

"I don't know. Let's let all the kids decide together."

* * *

The next day, we made up. Gadi and my friends asked for my forgiveness, and Gadi gave me the key to the new hiding place. After that, a discussion began on what to name the bonfire. The kids tried to convince me that we should still call it "Yudah's bonfire." They'd probably gotten it over the head from their parents about what they'd done to me and were regretting it.

But I refused.

"We should give it a name that will unite everyone."

One boy suggested "The Peace Bonfire"; another said it should be "The Bonfire of Forgiveness," and another, "Friendship Bonfire."

But of all people it was Gadi who came up with the winning name.

"I think this bonfire taught us all something," he said. "And that's thanks to two kids. One of them is called Yudah, but he doesn't agree to have the bonfire named for him. So I suggest we name the bonfire after the second kid. I don't think anyone will object. How about 'Ayal's Bonfire'?"

Everyone agreed it was a great idea.

We set out to collect wood. Ayal was with us to "help." At first, he insisted on calling the bonfire "Yudah's Bonfire" but he gradually got used to the idea that "Ayal's Bonfire" was a better name.

That Lag BaOmer, as the whole neighborhood gathered to watch, Ayal was handed the torch to light the bonfire.

But he was scared. He came over to me and whispered, "Help me."

I hesitated.

But then the other kids and their parents said, "Yudah, go ahead and help him."

Ayal and I walked over to the massive bonfire and lit it together. The pile of wood burst into flames that shot up high, lighting up the sky and lighting up our hearts with an unforgettable glow.

Glossary

The following glossary provides a partial explanation of some of the Hebrew, Yiddish, and Aramaic words and phrases used in this book. The spellings and definitions reflect the way the specific word is used in this book. There may be alternate spellings and meanings for the words.

achdus: unity.

baruch Hashem: thank G-d.

battim: the tefillin boxes into which the parchments are placed.

bechor: firstborn.

beis din: rabbinical court.

b'ezras Hashem: G-d willing.

chas v'chalilah: G-d forbid.

chas v'shalom: G-d forbid.

chevra (Y.): close-knit group.

chavrusas: study partners.

chayechah kodmim: your life comes first.

cherem: ban.

chinuch: education.

galus: exile.

gemach: collection of items loaned at no cost to the borrower.

hashgachah pratis: Divine providence.

lashon hara: a remark that belittles or harms another person; gossip.

l'to'eles: for a valid reason.

levayah: funeral.

middos: character traits.

min haShamayim: Heaven-sent.

nachas: pleasure; joy.

parshiyos: parchments placed inside tefillin.

Pirkei Avos: Ethics of the Fathers.

rasha: evil person.

ratzon Hashem: G-d's will.

rechilus: gossip.

sefer Torah: Torah scroll.

seudah: a meal.

seudas hodayah: a meal of thanksgiving.

Shir hama'alos, esa einai el heharim, me'ayin yavo ezri…: *Tehillim* 121:2: "I raise my eyes to the mountains [in prayer], 'From where will my help come?'"

sofer: a Jewish scribe of religious texts.

talmidim: students.

tehillah: psalm.

tehillim: psalms.

tzedakah: charity.

yiras Shamayim: fear of Heaven.

yetzer hara: evil inclination.

zechus: merit.

The CHAIM WALDER Children's Library

Kids Speak 1–10

Author and educator Chaim Walder opens a window into the world of children and youth, shedding light on the depths of their feelings and inner struggles. The *Kids Speak* series features a collection of stories by children describing their personal problems, their fears and their unusual experiences. Accompanied by the illustrations of Yoni Gerstein or Devora Benedict.

HIGHLIGHTS FROM VOLUME 10: **Gadi** is the most popular boy in class — until a meeting with a mask artist changes his life... **Rachelli** wants her *bas mitzvah* party to be the talk of the town. It is, but not in the way she thought... **Chezky** lacks self-confidence — until he attempts a mission harder than finding a needle in a haystack... **Naomi**'s grades are rock-bottom and her best friend Etty's are the same; their friendship falters when Etty decides to change. Fourteen boys and girls are the heroes of *Kids Speak 10*! 208 pp.

Stories Straight from Avi's Heart

A Collection of Stories for Young Children to Enrich Their Emotional World

Ahuva Raanan & Chaim Walder

From anger, sadness, and anxiety to happiness, excitement, and love, Avi's feelings — negative and positive — bring out life lessons in a way every child will relate to. Tirtsa Pelleg's captivating illustrations enhance Avi's stories, helping children learn their interactive lessons. 80 pp.

What Should You Do Now?

Helping Kids Find Solutions!

illustrated by Devorah Benedict

Ten stories of children facing common dilemmas, which guide toward a correct solution in a way that kids can enjoy. Reading about other children in familiar situations helps kids realize that their own challenges are normal and can be navigated successfully. 89 pp.

Stories Straight from Mommy's Heart

A Collection of Stories Which Strengthen the Emotional Bond Between Parents and Children

Ahuva Raanan & Chaim Walder

Sometimes Mommy feels worried, and sometimes she feels happy. This sequel to *Stories Straight from Avi's Heart* gives voice to the range of emotions that parents sometimes feel, giving children an understanding of what it is their parents are experiencing. 80 pp.

That's Me, Tzviki Green

"I'm the boy you heard about concerning the hostages in the Jerusalem supermarket. The story itself is true, but some of the reports were exaggerated..."

Meet Tzviki Green, a courageous boy from Israel uprooted from his comfortable, familiar home and transplanted to the frightening newness of America. Join Tzviki as he struggles and succeeds in many difficult challenges. 334 pp.

Animals Speak

Dovi Weinroth & Chaim Walder

Through 19 animal parables, children explore important values and virtues, such as courage, loyalty, self-control, inner strength, honesty, teamwork, thinking of others, and much more. Here is an effective way to help kids better understand, deal with, and give voice to their own emotions and dilemmas. 128 pp.

Our Heroes 1 & 2

Kids Follow in the Footsteps of the Past

Through first-person accounts of children who acted with good *middos* and nobility of spirit — following in the footsteps of our nation's spiritual giants — *Our Heroes* shows how every single girl and boy can be hero. 248 pp.

Team Taryag 1 & 2

Volume 1: Fire-X Flashlight Mystery

Volume 2: The Mystery of the Missing Amulet

Join **T**anchum, **R**euvi, **Y**israel, and **G**adi — *Team TaRYaG* — in their exciting adventures in this brand new series! A power-packed reading experience with over 100 full-color illustrations by Rotem Hadad Halevi! 374 pp.

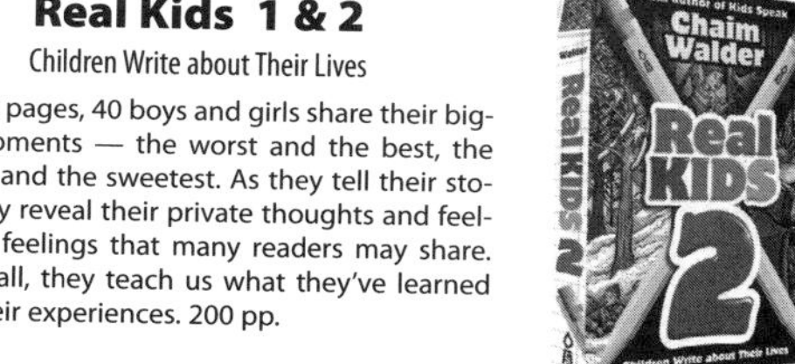

Real Kids 1 & 2

Children Write about Their Lives

In these pages, 40 boys and girls share their biggest moments — the worst and the best, the scariest and the sweetest. As they tell their stories, they reveal their private thoughts and feelings — feelings that many readers may share. Best of all, they teach us what they've learned from their experiences. 200 pp.